Answer Revision Questions for Higher Chemistry

C000231381

GEORGE WATSON'S COLLEGE
CHEMISTRY DEPARTMENT

J M Briggs

D A Buchanan
(Moray House Institute,
Edinburgh University)

J R Melrose
(Lenzie Academy, Lenzie, Glasgow)

Published by
Chemcord
Inch Keith
East Kilbride
Glasgow

ISBN 1 870570 75 8

© Briggs, Buchanan and Melrose, 2000
First reprint 2005

Typeset by J M Briggs
Printed by Bell and Bain Ltd, Glasgow

Contents

Note

The answers to questions marked with an asterisk,*, are for amended questions. Amendments take account of the relative atomic masses in the 1999 SQA Data Booklet for Chemistry Higher and Advanced Higher, and errors in the Revision Questions Book.
Amendments are as follows.

Exercise 1.1

5. a) omit

b) becomes a) etc.

Exercise 1.3

2. c) 202.2 g of KNO_3

7. b) 13.82 g of K_2CO_3

d) 6.605 g of $(NH_4)_2SO_4$

c) 15.96 g of $CuSO_4$

Exercise 1.5

2. 0.243 g of magnesium

5. 1.261 g of sodium sulphite

4. 1.321 g of ammonium sulphate

Exercise 1.15

14. c) i) replace "alkane" with "alkanol"

Exercise 1.16

2. a) 16.05 g of sulphur

3. b) 180 g of H_2O

4. b) 1.011 g of KNO_3

6. a) 9.42 g of K_2O

c) 0.001 g of carbon-12

d) 3.42 g of $C_{12}H_{22}O_{11}$

c) 10.39 g of Li_2SO_4

Exercise 1.17

1. replace "propene" with "propane"

Exercise 2.15

1. b) omit

Exercise 3.3

14. enthalpy changes are negative

Exercise 3.13

17. should be numbered 16.

Prescribed Practical Activities

1. a) omit "nickel plating"

Unit 1   Energy Matters

Exercise 1.1   Following the course of a reaction

1.

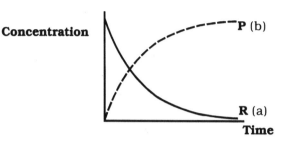

c) The steeper the gradient, the faster the reaction.

2. a) i) $0.1 \text{ mol } l^{-1}\text{min}^{-1}$ ii) $0.06 \text{ mol } l^{-1}\text{min}^{-1}$ iii) $0.035 \text{ mol } l^{-1}\text{min}^{-1}$
    b) i) The reaction rate decreases.
        ii) As the reaction proceeds the concentration of reactant decreases.

3. a) 72 cm^3
    b) i) 75 s   ii) 20 s
    iii) The reaction rate decreases as the concentration of acid decreases.
    c) $1.9 \text{ cm}^3\text{s}^{-1}$

4. a) One of the products is a gas.
    b)

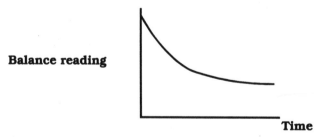

5*. a) 10 °C   b) 0.66 s^{-1}
     c) i) 25 s   ii) 12 s   iii) 6 s

6.

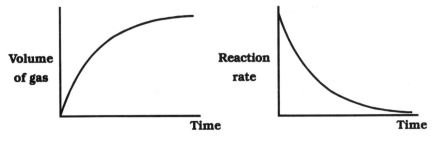

7. a) 0.0095 mol l^{-1} b) 9×10^{-6} mol l^{-1} s^{-1}

c) As the reaction proceeds, the concentration of methyl ethanoate and hydroxide ions falls and the reaction rate decreases.

8. a) The rate is greater at **X** than at **Y**.   d)
    b) 0.3 g min^{-1}
    c) 3.5 min

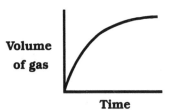

9. a) 0.16 s^{-1} b) 12.5 s   c) 25 s

Exercise 1.2   Factors affecting rate

1. a) The rate of production of hydrogen would be smaller.
    b) The rate of production of hydrogen would be unchanged.
    c) The rate of production of hydrogen would be greater.
    d) The rate of production of hydrogen would be greater.

2.

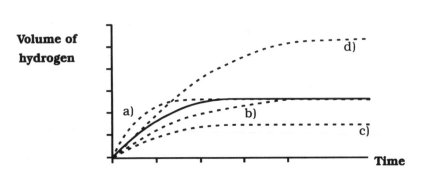

3.

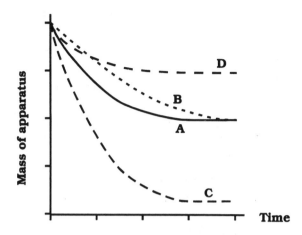

4. a) Collisions between molecules must have kinetic energy greater than the activation energy of the reaction.

    b) i) Increasing concentration increases the total number of collisions per second. The number of effective collisions will increase and the rate will be greater.

        ii) Increasing the particle size of a solid will decrease the surface area of the reactant and will decrease the number of effective collisions, decreasing the rate.

        iii) Increasing the temperature increases the number of collisions between molecules which have energy greater than the activation energy of the reaction.

5. a) i) $Mg(s) + 2HCl(aq) \rightarrow MgCl_2(aq) + H_2(g)$

        ii) $Zn(s) + 2HCl(aq) \rightarrow ZnCl_2(aq) + H_2(g)$

        iii) $2Na(s) + 2HCl(aq) \rightarrow NaCl(aq) + H_2(g)$

    b)

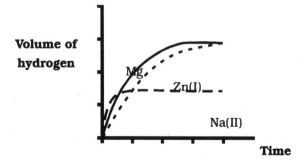

6. a)

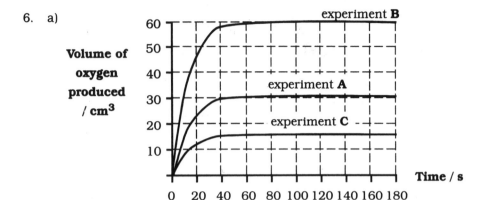

b) i) The volume of oxygen in the first 20 s would increase.

ii) no change

Assume that gas volumes are measured at the same temperature.

c)

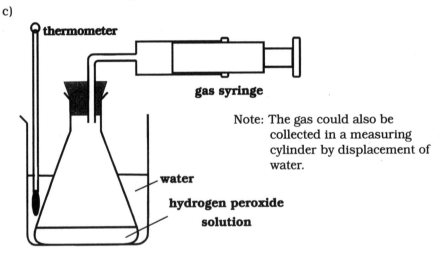

Note: The gas could also be collected in a measuring cylinder by displacement of water.

7. The particle size of the marble chips.
The concentration of the acid solution.
The temperature of the reactants.

8. a) 55 min

b) i) sample **A**   ii) sample **B**

c) The initial rate of reaction **B** is greater, hence the particle size is smaller.

9.

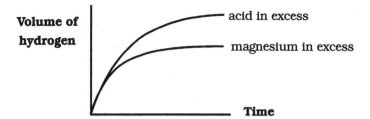

Volume of hydrogen — acid in excess — magnesium in excess — Time

10.

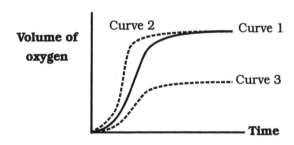

Volume of oxygen — Curve 2 — Curve 1 — Curve 3 — Time

11.

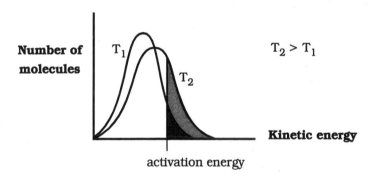

Number of molecules — T_1 — T_2 — $T_2 > T_1$ — Kinetic energy

activation energy

As the temperature is increased, the number of particles with energy equal to or greater than the activation energy of the reaction increases greatly (shown by the lightly shaded area of the graph). Hence the number of successful collisions increases and the rate of reaction becomes much greater.

12. a) The concentration of the iodate solution.
   b) i) The concentration of the sulphite solution.
      ii) It increases the rate of the reaction.

13. a) The total volume of the sodium thiosulphate solution.
   b) i) The reaction rate is directly proportional to the concentration of thiosulphate solution, ie. as the concentration of the solution decreases, the rate decreases.
      ii) As the concentration of thiosulphate ions increases, the number of collisions between thiosulphate ions and hydrogen ions increases. The number of effective collisions will therefore increase and the rate will increase.
   c) Increasing the temperature.

14. a) Hydrogen is produced in the reaction and lost to the atmosphere.
    b)

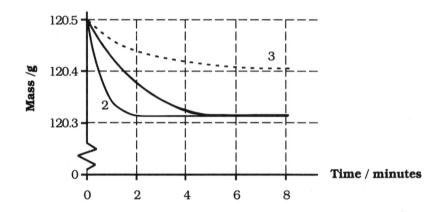

Exercise 1.3   Mole calculations

1. a) 160 g   b) 32.05 g   c) 212 g   d) 25.2 g

2. a) 0.1 mol   b) 0.5 mol   c)* 2 mol   d)* 0.05 mol

3. a) 0.2 mol   b) 0.25 mol   c) 0.2 mol   d) 0.4 mol

4. a) 2 mol l^{-1} b) 10 mol l^{-1} c) 2 mol l^{-1} d) 0.1mol l^{-1}

5. a) 2 litres   b) 200 cm^3 c) 200 cm^3 d) 200 cm^3

6. a) 14.92 g   b) 2.842 g   c) 3.7075 g   d) 4.8 g

7. a) 0.1 mol l^{-1} b)* 0.05 mol l^{-1} c)* 0.4 mol l^{-1} d) 1.25 mol l^{-1}

Exercise 1.4   Calculations based on equations

1. a) 12.6 g   b) 3.01 g   c) 1.64×10^3 kg
    d) 2.72×10^4 kg   e) 2.00 g

2. a) 0.5 mol   b) 6.25 cm^3 c) 0.430 mol l^{-1}

3. 37.0

4. 2.505 g

Exercise 1.5   The idea of excess

1. a) Zinc is in excess.   b) Magnesium is in excess.
    c) Zinc is in excess.   d) Magnesium is in excess.

2*. 0.403 g

3. 18 g

4*. 0.34 g

5*. 0.641 g

6. 0.153 g

7. 0.275 g

Exercise 1.6   Catalysts

1. a) i) To increase the surface area of the catalyst so that the reaction is faster.
        ii) Accept "The same products would form much more slowly."
            Note: Nitrogen and water are actually produced in this reaction.
    b) A catalyst in a different state of matter from the reactants, eg a solid catalyst for a reaction involving gases.

2. a) It lowers the activation energy of a reaction so that the reaction is faster.

   b) To increase the surface area of the catalyst to provide more sites at which a reaction may occur.

   c) The active sites of the catalyst are blocked so that the reaction can no longer occur on them.

3. a) As the solution turns from pink to green, a new activated complex is formed with a lower activation energy. The reaction becomes faster. As hydrogen peroxide is used up, the concentration of the activated complex decreases and the colour returns to pink.

   b) homogeneous

4. a) enzymes

   b) For example, fermentation of glucose by the enzyme, zymase, present in yeast.

5. a) To increase the surface area of catalyst exposed to harmful gases, so that they are converted more rapidly to harmless gases.

   b) heterogeneous

   c) For example, the reaction of oxides of nitrogen with carbon monoxide to produce nitrogen and carbon dioxide.

   d) Lead is deposited on the surface of the catalyst, poisoning the active sites and preventing the catalysed reaction from occurring.

6. a) For example, iron is used in the Haber process to convert nitrogen and hydrogen into ammonia.

   b) For example, the enzyme, zymase, present in yeast is used to convert glucose into carbon dioxide and ethanol during fermentation.

7.

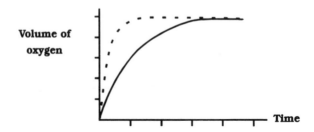

Exercise 1.7   Potential energy diagrams

1. a)   A reaction which releases energy to its surroundings.
    b)   A reaction which absorbs energy from its surroundings.

2. a)   -11.3 kJ mol^{-1}
    b)   exothermic

3. a)   i) $E_3 - E_2$
         ii) $E_2 - E_1$
    b)   i)   It would reduce the activation energy.
         ii) no change

4. a)   no change
    b)   It would increase the activation energy.

5. a)   i)   70 kJ mol^{-1} ii)   30 kJ mol^{-1} iii) 60 kJ mol^{-1}
         iv) 20 kJ mol^{-1}
    b)   i)   +40 kJ mol^{-1} ii)   -40 kJ mol^{-1}

6. a)

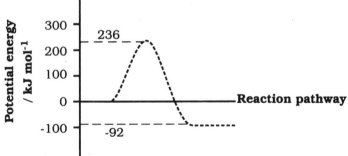

    b)   328 kJ mol^{-1}

7. a)   i)   **a+b**   ii)   **c**   iii) **b**
    b)   endothermic

8. a)

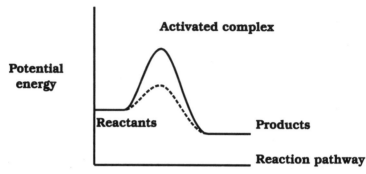

Activated complex

Potential energy

Reactants

Products

Reaction pathway

b) It is an unstable species formed at the potential energy maximum of the reaction pathway.

Exercise 1.8 Enthalpy changes

1. a) i) $CH_3OH(l) + 1\frac{1}{2}O_2(g) \rightarrow CO_2(g) + 2H_2O(l)$
   ii) $KOH(s) + H_2O(l) \rightarrow KOH(aq)$
   b) $H^+(aq) + OH^-(aq) \rightarrow H_2O(l)$

2. a) -1031 kJ mol^{-1}
   b) Heat energy is lost to the air, tripod stand and the beaker, so that the measured enthalpy change is much lower than the data booklet value. Incomplete combustion can also occur.

3. -1352 kJ mol^{-1}

4. -295.6 kJ mol^{-1}

5. a) i) The enthalpy of combustion increases regularly because an additional CH_2 group is burning to give 1 mol of CO_2 and 1 mol of H_2O as the homologous series progresses.
   ii) -2667 kJ mol^{-1}
   b) 33.67 kJ mol^{-1}
   c) In the combustion of dimethyl ether 6 CH bonds, and 2 CO bonds are broken whereas in ethanol, 1 CC bond, 1 CO bond and 5 CH bonds are broken. The energy required to break different bonds is different so that the energy required for bond breaking is different. The energy released in bond making is the same so the enthalpies of combustion will differ.

6. 21 kJ mol^{-1}

7. a) −39.6 kJ mol^{-1}
   b) Heat energy is lost to the surroundings by conduction through the metal beaker, by convection from the surface of the liquid, and because the thermal heat capacity of the beaker is not taken into account. Also, the specific heat capacity of the solution is not exactly the same as that of water.
   c) Use an expanded polystyrene beaker, with low heat capacity, good insulation properties, and fit a plastic lid to prevent heat loss by convection.

8. −42 kJ mol^{-1}

9. −1.93 °C

10. 57 kJ mol^{-1}

11. −57.1 kJ mol^{-1}

Exercise 1.9   Atomic and ionic size

1. a)

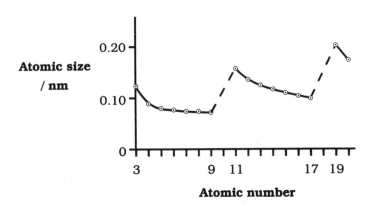

   b) The trend of the graph between the elements 3 to 9 is repeated between elements 11 to 17.

2. a) i) As the nuclear charge increases, electrons in the second energy level are attracted progressively closer to the nucleus.

   ii) The atomic size increases because 1 electron enters an energy level further away from the nucleus. Also, increased screening by inner electrons means that the full nuclear charge is not experienced by the outer electron.

   b) i) top right hand corner

   ii) bottom left hand corner

3. a) The electron in the third energy level of sodium is attracted by a nuclear charge of 11+, shielded by 10 electrons in the two inner energy levels. The 7 electrons in the third energy level of chlorine are attracted by a nuclear charge of 17+, shielded by 10 electrons in the two inner energy levels. The electrons of chlorine are therefore attracted closer to the nucleus.

   b) The sodium ion has electrons only in energy levels 1 and 2, but the chloride ion has a complete third energy level and therefore is bigger.

4. a) The 8 electrons in the second energy level of Na^+ are attracted by a nuclear charge of 11+. The 8 electrons in the second energy level of Mg^{2+} are attracted by a nuclear charge of 12+ and are therefore pulled closer to the nucleus.

   b) Ca^{2+} has a complete third energy level of electrons whereas Mg^{2+} has only a complete second energy level.

   c) The electrons in the full second energy level of F^- are attracted by a nuclear charge of 9+ whereas the electrons on the full second energy level of Na^+ are attracted by a nuclear charge of 11+.

5. a) Element 13 - 0.05 nm   Element 15 - 0.25 nm

   b) i) The radius of H^+ is the radius of the nucleus only.

   ii) The electrons in the full first energy level of H^- are attracted by a nuclear charge of 1+ whereas the electrons of Li^+ are attracted by a nuclear charge of 3+.

   c) B^{3+} has only a complete first energy level. N^{3-} has a complete second energy level and is therefore larger.

6. a) The ions are smaller because electrons have been removed from the third energy level to form the ion.

    b) P^{3-} has a full third energy level, whereas Si^{4+} has only a full second energy level.

    c) They have 8 electrons in the second energy level.

    d) As the nuclear charge increases, the electrons, all in the second energy level, are attracted closer to the nucleus.

Exercise 1.10   Ionisation energy and electronegativity

1   a) The energy require to remove 1 mol of electrons from 1 mol of atoms in the gaseous state.

    b) i)   endothermic

        ii) Energy must be supplied to overcome the attraction between the electron and the nucleus.

    c) $Na(g) \rightarrow Na^+(g) + e^-$ $\Delta H = +502$ kJ mol^{-1}

            $Ca(g) \rightarrow Ca^+(g) + e^-$ $\Delta H = +596$ kJ mol^{-1}

    d) See part c).

2. a) i) $Mg^+(g) \rightarrow Mg^{2+}(g) + e^-$ $\Delta H = +1460$ kJ mol^{-1}

        ii) $Al^{2+}(g) \rightarrow Al^{3+}(g) + e^-$ $\Delta H = +2760$ kJ mol^{-1}

    b) See part a).

3. a)

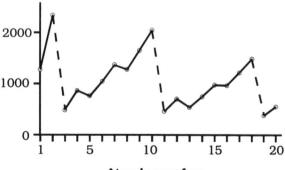

    b) The pattern between elements 3 and 10 is repeated between elements 11 and 18.

4. a) The first ionisation energy decreases because an electron is being removed from an energy level further away from the nucleus. Also, the pull on the outer electron by the nucleus is less due to screening by inner electrons.

    b) The first ionisation energies are low because an electron is being removed from an energy level containing only 1 electron. The second ionisation energy is very high because an electron is being removed from a complete energy level closer to the nucleus.

    c) Lithium has only 3 electrons.

5. The first ionisation energies increase going from sodium to aluminium because electrons are being removed from the third energy level and the nuclear charge is increasing from sodium to aluminium. (There is a decrease between magnesium and aluminium resulting from differences in the sub-shells of the elements.)

6. a) In each period the alkali metal has 1 electron in its outermost energy level, attracted by a smaller nuclear charge than attracts the 7 electrons in the same energy level of the corresponding halogen. The ionisation energy of the alkali metal is therefore much lower.

    b) The second ionisation energy of an alkali metal is much higher than the second ionisation energy of the corresponding halogen because the second electron of the alkali metal is being removed from a complete energy level closer to the nucleus.

7. a) 5174 kJ mol^{-1}

    b) 7500 kJ mol^{-1}

8. a) Li, Na, K

    b) Group 1

    c) The electron in the first energy level is attracted by a smaller nuclear charge than any other element in the same period.

9. a) **D**   b) **A** and **E**   c) **B**   d) **C**

10. a) He and Ne   b) noble gases
    c) They have complete outermost energy levels in which electrons are attracted by the highest nuclear charge of any element in the same period.

11. a) alkali metals
    b) The second electron is removed from a complete energy level which is much closer to the nucleus and requires much more energy.

12. The third ionisation energy of magnesium requires the removal of an electron from the complete second energy level which is close to the nucleus. This requires very high energy. The third ionisation of aluminium removes an electron from the third energy level and requires much less energy.

13. a) noble gases   b) i) **I, Q**   ii) **C, K, S**
    c) The electrons of **L** are attracted by a much greater nuclear charge than those of **K**.
    d) The second ionisation energy of **L** represents removal of the second electron from the third energy level, whereas that of **K** represents removal of an electron from the full second energy level.

14. a) Helium has 2 electrons, hydrogen has only 1.
    b) Helium has a greater nuclear charge and attracts electrons more strongly.

15. a)

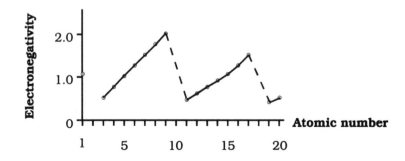

    b) The pattern between elements 3 and 10 is repeated between elements 11 and 18.

16. a) The electrons in the outermost energy level of the Group 7 elements are further away from the nucleus on going down the group and are more effectively screened by electrons in inner energy levels.The electrons are attracted less strongly towards the nucleus, hence the electronegativities of the elements get progressively smaller.

b) The electronegativity of the elements increase because the nuclear charges of the elements increase from sodium to aluminium. Electrons in the third energy level are therefore attracted more strongly towards the nucleus and the electronegativity increases.

c) noble gases

Exercise 1.11   Types of bonding and structure

1. The electron cloud corresponding to the first energy level of hydrogen and an electron cloud of the third energy level of sulphur overlap. The shared pair of electrons constitutes a covalent single bond. Sulphur needs to form 2 covalent single bonds to form a stable molecule of hydrogen sulphide. By sharing electrons, both hydrogen atoms and the sulphur atom complete their outermost energy levels.

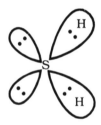

2. a) A polar covalent bond forms in hydrogen fluoride when the shared pair of electrons in the overlapped electron clouds from the hydrogen atom and the fluorine atom are shared unequally. The very high electronegativity of fluorine causes the electrons to move closer to the fluorine nucleus polarising the bond.

b) H-F is more polar.

c) F has a higher electronegativity than Cl, hence electrons are drawn more strongly along the halogen - hydrogen bond towards F than towards Cl giving a more polar bond.

3. a) endothermic

    b) i) The positive and negative ions are attracted to each other and form a lattice in which positive ions are surrounded by negative ions and vice versa.

       ii) exothermic

4. a) chlorine, fluorine, oxygen, nitrogen chloride

    b) hydrogen oxide, hydrogen sulphide

    c) sodium fluoride, potassium chloride, lithium oxide

5. Nitrogen and hydrogen are both diatomic elements. Electrons are equally shared between the nitrogen atoms in N_2 and between the hydrogen atoms in H_2.
In ammonia, electrons are drawn strongly towards the nitrogen atom along the N-H single bonds because nitrogen has a higher electronegativity than hydrogen, hence the bonds are polarised.

6. Carbon and sulphur have equal electronegativities, hence each exerts the same pull on the electrons in covalent bonds so that the sharing of electrons is equal.

7. a) lithium and fluorine

    b) These elements have the greatest difference in electronegativity of any pair of elements in the period.

8. Fluorine has the highest electronegativity of any of the halogens. The electronegativity difference betwen rubidium and fluorine is greatest and hence will give the most ionic of the halides of rubidium.

9. A type of bonding in which delocalised electrons are shared between huge numbers of atoms and are responsible for holding together a lattice of metal atoms.

10. a) A lattice in which many atoms are held together by a network of covalent bonds extending in 3 dimensions.

    b) i) covalent bonds   ii) van der Waals' forces.

11. a) metallic bonds   b) ionic bonds

Exercise 1.12   Intermolecular forces of attraction

1 a) Weak forces of attraction between neighbouring molecules.
   b) It is a result of the instantaneous polarisation of the electrons of one molecule inducing polarisation in the electrons of a neighbouring molecule so that there is a momentary force of attraction between the molecules.
   c) The strength of van der Waals' forces increases going down the group.

2. a) Hydrogen bonding forces are much stronger than van der Waals' forces.
   b) Hydrogen bonding forces are much weaker than covalent bonds.

3.

Van der Waals' forces occur; no permanent dipole - permanent dipole interactions; no hydrogen bonding	Permanent dipole - permanent dipole interactions occur; no hydrogen bonding	Hydrogen bonding occurs
H_2 Cl_2 N_2 NCl_3	PH_3 HBr	HF H_2O NH_3

4. In hydrogen gas, the H-H bond is not polarised, hence there are only weak van der Waals' forces between neighbouring molecules. In NH_3, the N-H bonds are very strongly polarised and the positively polarised hydrogen atoms of one molecule can interact strongly with the negatively polarised nitrogen atoms of neighbouring molecules so that hydrogen bonding occurs.

5. The relative molecular mass of hydrogen fluoride is 20. The existence of molecules with relative molecular masses 40 and 60 indicates the formation of dimers and trimers of HF held together by hydrogen bonding.

Exercise 1.13   Polarity of molecules

1. A polar molecule has a definite polarity because the bond dipoles do not cancel out. A polar bond has a polarity resulting from the unequal attraction of the electron pairs in the bond by the nuclei which form the bond.

2. a) polar   b) non-polar
   c) polar   d) non-polar

3. The water molecule has a bent shape. The polarities of the bond dipoles combine to give a definite polarity for the molecule. Carbon dioxide is a linear molecule. The C-O bond polarities are opposed at 180 ° and cancel each other out.

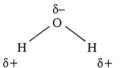 $$\delta- \quad \delta+ \quad \delta-$$ $$O = C = O$$

4. a) The liquids in group **A** have polar molecules, but those in group **B** are non-polar.
   b) Tetrachloromethane would not deflect because it has tetrahedral symmetry and the C-Cl bond dipoles cancel each other out.

5. In molecule **A**, the dipoles are not opposed to each other, but in molecule **B** the dipoles are opposed to each other at 180 ° and cancel each other out.

Exercise 1.14   Bonding and structure - the elements

1   a)   hydrogen or any Group 7 element
     b)   oxygen
     c)   nitrogen
     d)   phosphorus
     e)   sulphur

2.   a)   b)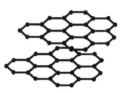

3.   a)   An array containing an indefinite number of atoms held together to
          form a 3-dimensional network by covalent bonds.
     b)   A molecule which contains a fixed number of atoms.
     c)   A substance whose molecules contain only 1 atom.

4.   a)   The electrons in the outermost energy levels of the atoms in a metal
          are free to move from atom to atom and are not associated with one
          particular atom.
     b)   Since electrons are free to move between atoms in both the solid and
          liquid states, electricity can flow easily through the metal.

5.   The fullerene structure, C_{60}, is a discrete molecule in which 60 carbon
     atoms form a ball shaped molecule of hexagons and pentagons. Diamond
     is a covalent network of carbon atoms in which each carbon atom is
     surrounded tetrahedrally by four nearest neighbours. The molecule has
     no fixed size.

6.   a)   pure covalent single bonds, discrete diatomic molecules
     b)   pure covalent single bonds, discrete molecular, 8 atoms per molecule
     c)   metallic solid
     d)   network covalent solid

7.

Type	Bonding and structure at normal room temperature and pressure
Type E	Monatomic gases
Type B	Covalent network solids
Type D	Diatomic covalent gases
Type C	Discrete covalent molecular solids
Type A	Metallic lattice solids

Exercise 1.15   Properties of substances

1. a) covalent network solid
    b) It has a very high melting point but contains no charged particles when molten.

2. disagree
    Ionic bonds are broken when an ionic compound melts, but only weak intermolecular forces are broken when a covalent substance melts. The covalent bonds of the molecule are **not** broken.

3. covalent
    $TiCl_4$ has a very low boiling point and melting point. It is unlikely to contain ionic bonds which are strong and require a lot of energy to break.

4. The lithium halides are ionic solids. The melting points decrease because the strength of the ionic bonds decrease.

5. PCl_3 has a discrete molecular covalent structure and has only weak forces between its molecules. NaCl is an ionic solid and has strong ionic bonds between all neighbouring ions in its lattice.

6. As the halogen molecules become larger, the molecules are more easily polarised and the van der Waals' forces between them increase so that their boiling points increase.

7. a) HI has a higher relative molecular mass and therefore stronger van der Waals' forces between its molecules.

    b) 150 K

    c) HF is very strongly polarised and its molecules can hydrogen bond together giving an unusually high boiling point.

8. a) methanol, hydrazine

    b) It is a relatively strong intermolecular force which make the molecules more difficult to separate.

    c) So that the van der Waals' forces are comparable.

    d) For example, melting point, viscosity, surface tension.

9. Liquid phosphine PH_3 has a low boiling point because the forces holding molecules together are weak van der Waals' forces. Liquid ammonia, which has a lower molecular mass, has a much higher boiling point because hydrogen bonding can occur between its much more polar molecules.

10. The sulphur hydrogen bond is not suffiiently polarised to allow hydogen bonding to occur between H_2S molecules. The O-H bonds in H_2O_2 are much more polarised and hydrogen bonding can occur giving an unusually high boiling point.

11. a) $\mathbf{X} = NH_3$ $\mathbf{Y} = CH_4$

    b) As the molecular mass of the hydride increases, the polarisability of the molecule increases, the strength of the van der Waals' forces increases and the boiling point increases.

    c) Hydrogen bonding can occur between molecules in water and ammonia.

12. Propan-1-ol will have the higher boiling point because the O-H bond is so strongly polarised that hydrogen bonding can occur. In methoyxethane only van der Waals' forces can occur.

13. ethanol < ethan-1,2-diol < propan-1,2,3-triol

14. a) The molecules are larger, more polarisable, and therefore the van der Waals' forces are larger.
    b) alkanols
    c) i)   propan-1-ol
        ii) Propan-1-ol and butane have very similar relative molecular masses.

15. a) In octane the only forces between molecules are van der Waals' forces but in maleic and fumaric acids, hydrogen bonding can occur giving much higher melting points.
    b) Fumaric acid has a much more open structure which allows more extensive hydrogen bonding between neighbouring molecules. The shape of maleic acid ensures that 1 -OH group is involved in hydrogen bonding within the molecule, so that hydrogen bonding to neighbouring molecules is less extensive.

16. a) Diamond is made up of a network of carbon atoms each forming four single bonds to neighbouring carbon atoms. This gives a rigid structure of enormous hadness. All the outer energy level electrons of carbon are in localised covalent single bonds and are not free to move, hence diamond is a non-conductor.
    b) Graphite is made up of planes of carbon atoms in which 3 carbon atoms join to a central atom by covalent bonding. 1 electron of each carbon atom is not involved in forming single bonds and these electrons are delocalised over the whole plane of carbon atoms. Because the electrons are free to move, graphite conducts electricity. The planes of carbon atoms are held together by van der Waals' forces and are relatively easily separated. Graphite is therefore soft.
    c) Graphite is an effective lubricant because the planes of carbon atoms are free to slide past each other. (This is helped by molecules of air which are trapped between the graphite planes and separate them further reducing the strength of the van der Waals' forces. In partial vacuum graphite is much less effective as a lubricant.)

17. a) Covalent network elements in the solid state contain many atoms joined by strong covalent bonds. These are the bonds which are broken on melting, hence the melting points are very high.
    b) Discrete molecular solids are made up of small molecules which are held together by relatively weak van der Waals' forces. These are easily broken and the melting points are relatively low.

18. a) Period 3 (Na to Ar)

 b) Element **B** has 3 outer energy level electrons compared with only 1 for element **A**. Since more electrons are involved in metallic bonding, the bonding is stronger and the melting point is higher.

 c) **D** is a network covalent solid. It is the very strong covalent bonds between atoms which are broken on melting. **E** is discrete molecular and only weak van der Waals' forces between molecules are broken on melting.

19. a) Chlorine and phosphorus have low melting points because they have discrete molecular structures with molecules held together by weak van der Waals' forces.

 b) Magnesium forms a latice held together by strong metallic bonding. Silicon has a network covalent structure.

20. a) i) Li 181 °C   ii) Na 98 °C   iii) K 64 °C

 b) i) The metallic bonds decrease in strength.

  ii) The electrons involved in forming metallic bonds are progressively further from the nuclei they are holding together, hence the bonding is weaker.

21. a) The positive and negative ions of potassium chloride can interact strongly with the dipoles of surrounding water molecules. This releases energy which compensates for the energy requires to break up the lattice. Cyclohexane is non-polar and does not interact strongly enough with potassium chloride's ions to break up the lattice.

 b) Tetrachloromethane dissolves in hexane because new van der Waals' forces between tetrachloromethane and hexane can replace the van der Waals' forces broken in the pure liquids when they mix. If tetrachloromethane dissolved in water, it would break the hydrogen bonds between water molecules. There is no strong interaction between water molecules and tetrachloromethane to release energy to compensate for breaking the hydrogen bonds of water hence mixing is unlikely to occur.

22. Lithium iodide is significantly more covalent in character than caesium chloride which is ionic.

23. Water is made up of highly polar, non-linear molecules. When a water molecule approaches a positive sodium ion, the oxygen atom is more strongly attracted to the ion and comes closer to it than the hydrogen atoms. This attraction releases energy. A sodium ion can be surrounded on all sides by water molecules and this releases enough energy to compensate for the energy needed to remove the positive ion from the sodium chloride lattice from which it came.

When a water molecule approaches a negative chloride ion, the water molecule flips over and sits with hydrogen atoms closer to the ion. The negative ion can be surrounded by water molecules and the release of energy generated by the attraction is enough to compensate for the energy required to remove the negative ion from the lattice in the first place.

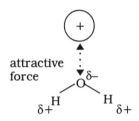

24. Boron and carbon are covalent network solids. Covalent bonds are broken on melting hence the very high melting points. Nitrogen, oxygen and fluorine have diatomic molecules held to each other by only weak van der Waals' forces. It is these weak forces which are broken on melting.

25. Methanol contains an -OH group, and its molecules can hydrogen bond to each. Since hydrogen bonds are relatively strong intermolecular forces, methanol has a much higher boiling point than expected.

26. a) FCl   b) LiCl   c) $BeCl_2$
    d) i) The polarity decreases.
        ii) The electronegativity of **X** at the left hand side of the table is smaller than that of chlorine, but at the right hand side, fluorine has a greater electronegativity than chlorine.

27. **A** covalent discrete molecular   **B** metallic
    C ionic   **D** covalent network

28. Poly(ethenol) has many -OH groups per molecule and can form hydrogen bonds with surounding water molecules, releasing energy which will allow the polymer to dissolve. Polyethene has no -OH groups and cannot interact strongly enough with water molecules to make dissolving energetically feasible.

29. Tin iodide is soluble in non-poler tetrachloromethane.
    Tin iodide has a low melting point.

Exercise 1.16   The Avogadro Constant

1. a) 1 mol   b) 8 mol   c) 0.2 mol   d) 3 mol

2, a)* 3×10^{23} b) 1.5×10^{24}
    c)* 5×10^{19} d) 3×10^{23}

3. a) 1.5×10^{22} b)* 6×10^{24}
    c) 1.2×10^{23} d)* 6×10^{21}

4. a) 6×10^{22} b)* 6×10^{21} c)* 6×10^{22} d) 1.5×10^{25}

5. a) 1.8×10^{23} b) 1.2×10^{24}
    c) 4.8×10^{23} d) 1.08×10^{24}

6. a)* 1.8×10^{23} b) 3.6×10^{23}
    c) 1.2×10^{25} d) 3×10^{27}

7. 24.52 g

8. 1.5×10^{23}

9. 6×10^{22}

10. 2.4×10^{23}

Exercise 1.17   Molar volumes of gases

1.* 47.2 litres   2. 92.8 litres   3. 24.0 litres

4. 17   5. 23.6 litres mol^{-1}

6. a) 11.5 litres   b) 2.3 litres

7. a) 6×10^{22} molecules   b) 1.2×10^{24} molecules

8. 1 mol = 35 g   PH$_3$

9. 0.8 g He   0.4 g H$_2$

10. a) 111.1 litres   b) 5.56 litres

11. a) 0.5 mol   b) 0.43 mol

12. a) 4.64 litres   b) 2.9 litres   c) 1.55 g

    d) 0.17 g   e) 2.33×10^5 litres   f) 1080 litres

Exercise 1.18   Calculations involving volumes

1. a) 1:1   b) 2:1   c) 1:2   d) 2:1   e) 1:1

2. 200 cm^3

3. i)   a) 200 cm^3 b) 100 cm^3
    ii)   a) 1 litre   b) 2 litres
    iii) a) 750 cm^3 b) 500 cm^3
    iv)   a) 975 cm^3 b) 600 cm^3

4. 55 cm^3 made up of 25 cm^3 O$_2$ and 30 cm^3 CO$_2$

5. a) $2CO(g) + O_2(g) \rightarrow 2CO_2(g)$

   b) i) carbon dioxide   ii) 80 cm^3 iii) 110 cm^3

6. 250 cm^3

7. a) $Xe(g) + 3F_2(g) \rightarrow XeF_6(s)$

   b) 250 cm^3 unreacted F_2 only

8. $40 \text{ cm}^3 CO_2(g)$ only

9. 750 cm^3 gas made up of $300 \text{ cm}^3 CO_2(g)$ and 450 cm^3 unreacted $O_2(g)$

10. $x = 3$ $y = 6$

11. a) 100 cm^3

    b) $50 \text{ cm}^3 CO_2(g)$ and $150 \text{ cm}^3 H_2O(g)$

    c) 150 cm^3 (ignoring contraction due to temperature change)

12. a) 120 cm^3

    b) C_6H_{10}

Unit 2   The World of Carbon

Exercise 2.1   Fuels

1. a) reforming
    b) i) To improve the efficiency of combustion.
        ii) The products are branched-chain, cyclic and aromatic
             hydrocarbons which burn more efficiently.
    c) **C**

2. a) Changing the structure of the carbon skeleton of a molecule.
    b) naphtha

3. a) i) Nitrogen oxides form from molecules of nitrogen and oxygen in
             the air/fuel mixture. The sparking of the ignition provides the
             activation energy necessary to allow nitrogen and oxygen to
             combine.
        ii) Carbon monoxide is formed by the incomplete combustion of
             hydrocarbons in a limited supply of air.
    b) carbon dioxide and nitrogen

4. a) A discharge of electricity in the spark plug.
    b) So that the fuel is more volatile at low temperatures.
    c) So that lead compounds can be omitted from the blend of petrol.

5. a) A substance which burns in air to release energy.
    b) i) fermentation (incomplete respiration)
        ii) The source of ethanol, sugar cane, is a renewable resource.

6. a) Conditions where air is absent.
    b) fermentation   c) methane

7. a) Only water vapour is released to the amosphere when hydrogen
        burns. Petrol releases carbon dioxide and carbon monoxide also.
    b) For example, methanol can be produced from synthesis gas and helps
        conserve oil supplies, methanol is less volatile than petrol and so is
        less likely to explode in a car collision.
        For example, methanol is toxic, it is difficult to get methanol to mix
        with petrol.

Exercise 2.2   Nomenclature and structural formulae - hydrocarbons

1. a) 2-methylpentane
    b) 2,3-dimethylbutane
    c) 3-methylpentane
    d) 2,2dimethylbutane
    e) 3,3-dimethylbut-1-ene
    f) 4-ethyl,5-methylhex-1-yne
    g) 2-ethyl,5-methylhex-2-ene
    h) 2-ethylbut-1-ene
    i) methylcyclobutane
    j) 1,2-dimethylcyclohexane
    k) 1,5-dimethylcyclopentene
    l) methylbut-1-yne

2. a)

$$CH_3-CH_2-\underset{\underset{CH_3}{|}}{\overset{\overset{CH_3}{|}}{C}}-CH_2-CH_3 \qquad \text{3,3-dimethylpentane}$$

   b)

$$CH_3-\underset{\underset{}{}}{\overset{\overset{CH_3}{|}}{CH}}-\overset{\overset{CH_3}{|}}{CH}-\overset{\overset{CH_3}{|}}{CH}-CH_3 \qquad \text{2,3,4-trimethylpentane}$$

   c)

$$CH_3-\underset{\underset{CH_3}{|}}{\overset{\overset{CH_3}{|}}{C}}-CH_3 \qquad \text{dimethylpropane}$$

   d) $CH_2=CH-CH_2-CH_3 \qquad$ but-1-ene

   e) $CH_3-CH_2-C\equiv C-CH_3 \qquad$ pent-2-yne

   f)

$$CH_3-\underset{\underset{CH_3}{|}}{\overset{\overset{CH_3}{|}}{C}}-CH=CH_2 \qquad \text{3,3-dimethylbut-1-ene}$$

   g)

$$CH_3-\overset{\overset{CH_3}{|}}{C}=CH_2 \qquad \text{methylpropene}$$

   h)

$$CH\equiv C-\underset{\underset{CH_3}{|}}{\overset{\overset{CH_3}{|}}{C}}-CH_2-CH_3 \qquad \text{3,3-dimethylpent-1-yne}$$

i)

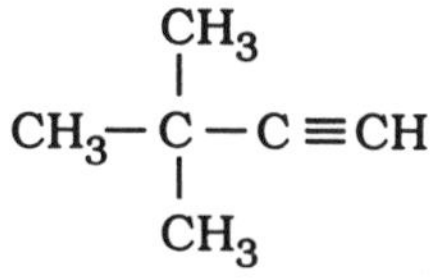

$$CH_3-\underset{\underset{CH_3}{|}}{\overset{\overset{CH_3}{|}}{C}}-C\equiv CH$$

3,3-dimethylbut-1-yne

3. a) 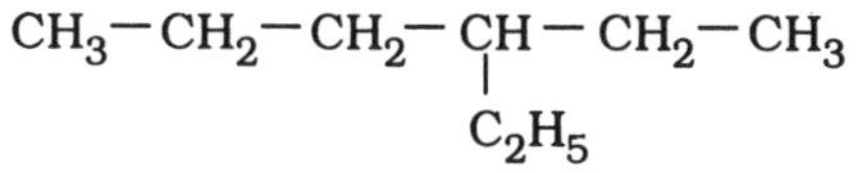 $CH_3-CH_2-CH_2-\underset{\underset{C_2H_5}{|}}{CH}-CH_2-CH_3$

   b)

$$CH_3-\underset{\underset{CH_3}{|}}{\overset{\overset{CH_3}{|}}{C}}-CH_2-\underset{\underset{CH_3}{|}}{CH}-CH_3$$

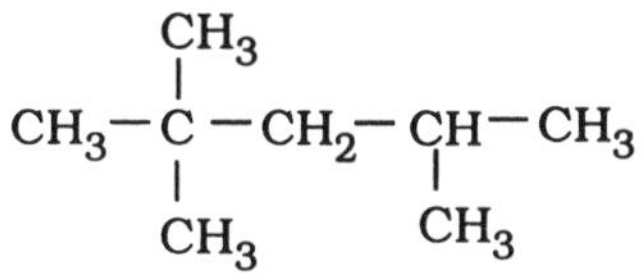

   c) $CH_3-\underset{\underset{CH_3}{|}}{CH}-\underset{\underset{C_2H_5}{|}}{CH}-CH_2-CH_3$

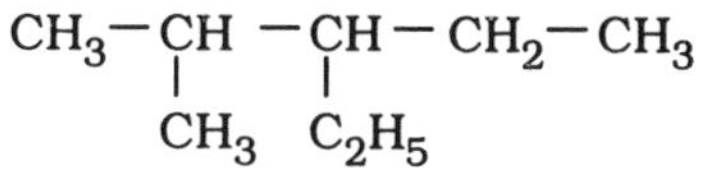

   d) $CH_2=CH-CH_2-CH_2-CH_3$

   e)

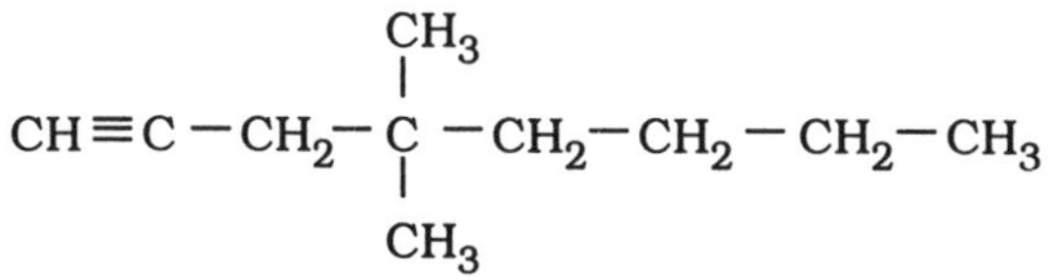

$$CH\equiv C-CH_2-\underset{\underset{CH_3}{|}}{\overset{\overset{CH_3}{|}}{C}}-CH_2-CH_2-CH_2-CH_3$$

   f) 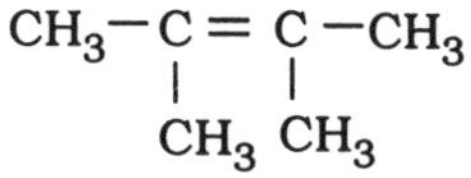 $CH_3-\underset{\underset{CH_3}{|}}{C}=\underset{\underset{CH_3}{|}}{C}-CH_3$

   g) 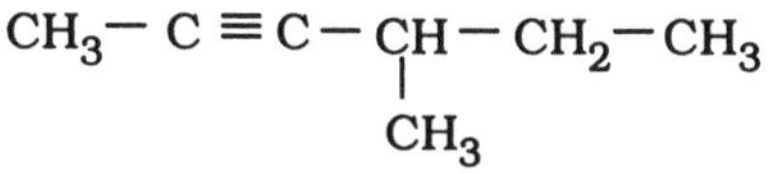 $CH_3-C\equiv C-\underset{\underset{CH_3}{|}}{CH}-CH_2-CH_3$

   h) $CH_2=CH-CH=CH-CH_3$

i)

$$CH_2 \diagdown^{CH_2}\diagup CH_2$$

i)
$$\begin{array}{c} \quad\;\; CH_2 \\ CH_2 \qquad CH_2 \\ \mid \qquad\quad \mid \\ CH_2 \qquad CH-C_2H_5 \\ \quad\; CH_2 \end{array}$$

j)
$$\begin{array}{c} \quad CH_2 \\ CH_2 \qquad CH_2 \\ \backslash \qquad\quad \diagup \\ CH=CH \end{array}$$

k)
$$\begin{array}{c} \quad CH-CH_3 \\ CH_2 \qquad\quad CH_2 \\ \backslash \qquad\qquad \diagup \\ CH_2-CH-CH_3 \end{array}$$

4. a)
$$CH_2=CH-CH_2-CH_2-CH_2-CH_3$$

$$CH_3-CH=CH-CH_2-CH_2-CH_3$$

$$CH_3-CH_2-CH=CH-CH_2-CH_3$$

b)
$$CH\equiv C-CH_2-CH_2-CH_3$$

$$CH_3-C\equiv C-CH_2-CH_3$$

c)
$$CH_3-CH_2-CH_2-CH_2-CH_3$$

$$CH_3-CH_2-\underset{\underset{CH_3}{\mid}}{CH}-CH_3$$

$$CH_3-\underset{\underset{CH_3}{\mid}}{\overset{\overset{CH_3}{\mid}}{C}}-CH_3$$

d) $CH_2=CH-CH_2-CH_3$ $CH_3-\underset{\underset{\displaystyle CH_3}{|}}{C}=CH_2$

   $CH_3-CH=CH-CH_3$

   $\underset{\displaystyle CH_2-CH_2}{\overset{\displaystyle CH_2-CH_2}{|\qquad|}}$ $\underset{\displaystyle CH_2-CH-CH_3}{\overset{\displaystyle CH_2}{\diagup\quad\diagdown}}$

Exercise 2.3   Nomenclature and structural formulae - alkanols

1. a) ethanol   b) butan-2-ol
   c) 2-methylbutan-2-ol   d) 4-methylpentan-2-ol

2. a) $CH_3-CH_2-CH_2-OH$ propan-1-ol

   b) $CH_3-\underset{\underset{\displaystyle OH}{|}}{CH}-CH_3$ propan-2-ol

   c)
       $CH_3-CH_2-\underset{\underset{\displaystyle OH}{|}}{\overset{\overset{\displaystyle CH_3}{|}}{C}}-CH_2-CH_3$ 3-methylpentan-3-ol

   d)
       $CH_3-\underset{\underset{\displaystyle OH}{|}}{CH}-\underset{\underset{\displaystyle CH_3}{|}}{CH}-CH_3$ 3-methylbutan-2-ol

3. a) $CH_3-CH_2-CH_2-CH_2-OH$

   b) $CH_3-CH_2-CH_2-\underset{\underset{\displaystyle OH}{|}}{CH}-\underset{\underset{\displaystyle CH_3}{|}}{CH}-CH_3$

   c) $CH_3-CH_2-\underset{\underset{\displaystyle CH_3}{|}}{CH}-\underset{\underset{\displaystyle CH_3}{|}}{CH}-CH_2-OH$

d)

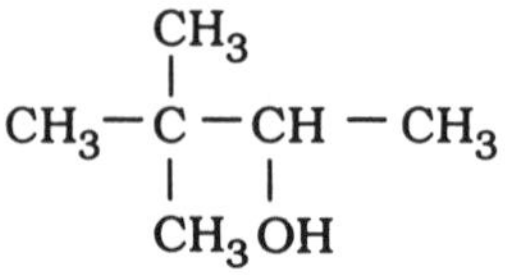

$$CH_3-\overset{\overset{\displaystyle CH_3}{|}}{C}-\overset{\overset{\displaystyle }{|}}{CH}-CH_3$$
$$\underset{CH_3\;\;OH}{|\;\;\;\;|}$$

4. a)

$$H-\overset{\overset{\displaystyle H}{|}}{C}-\overset{\overset{\displaystyle H}{|}}{C}-H$$
$$\underset{OH\;\;OH}{|\;\;\;\;|}$$

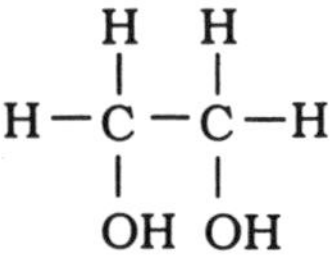

b) An alcohol with two -OH functional groups.

5. a) $CH_3-CH_2-CH_2-CH_2-OH$ $CH_3-CH_2-\underset{\overset{|}{OH}}{CH}-CH_3$

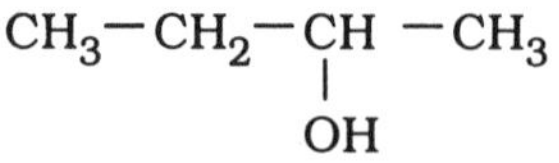

b)

$$CH_3-\overset{\overset{\displaystyle CH_3}{|}}{CH}-CH_2-OH$$

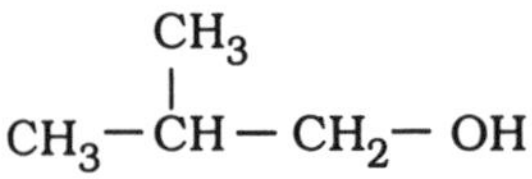

Exercise 2.4   Nomenclature and structural formulae - alkanals, alkanones and alkanoic acids

1. a) propanal   b) pentan-2-one
   c) 3-methylbutanal   d) 4,4-dimethylpentan-2-one

2. a) 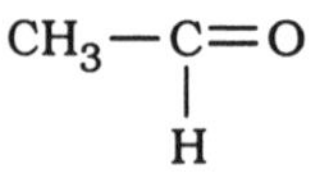 $CH_3-\underset{\overset{|}{H}}{C}=O$ ethanal

   b) 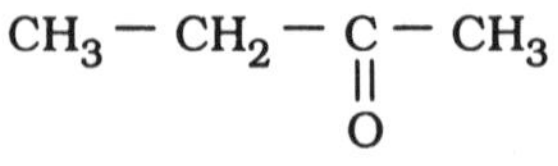 $CH_3-CH_2-\overset{\overset{\displaystyle }{}}{\underset{\underset{\displaystyle O}{||}}{C}}-CH_3$ butanone

   c) 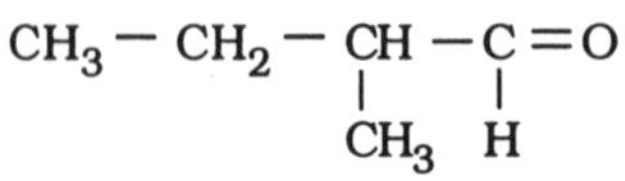 $CH_3-CH_2-\underset{\overset{|}{CH_3}}{CH}-\underset{\overset{|}{H}}{C}=O$ 2-methylbutanal

d)

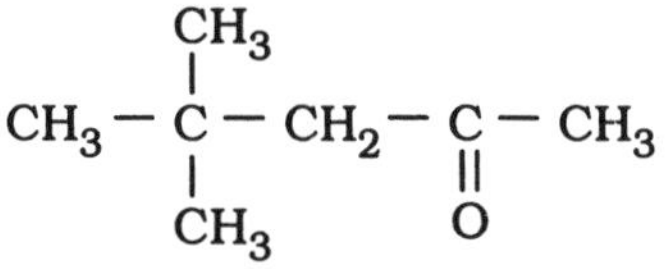

$$CH_3-\underset{\underset{CH_3}{|}}{\overset{\overset{CH_3}{|}}{C}}-CH_2-\underset{\overset{||}{O}}{C}-CH_3 \qquad \text{4,4-dimethylpentan-2-one}$$

3. a) 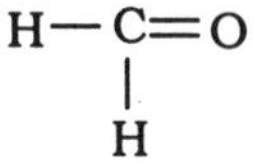
$$H-\underset{H}{\overset{|}{C}}{=}O$$

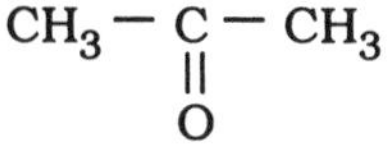

b)
$$CH_3-\underset{\overset{||}{O}}{C}-CH_3$$

c)
$$CH_3-CH_2-CH_2-\underset{\underset{C_2H_5}{|}}{CH}-CH_2-\underset{H}{\overset{|}{C}}{=}O$$

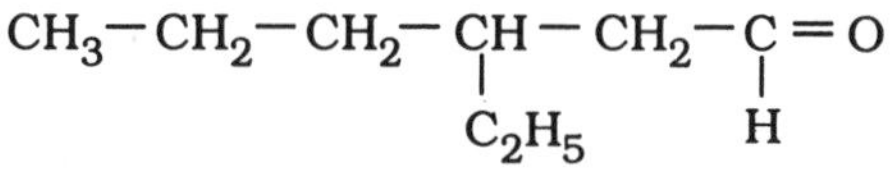

d)

$$CH_3-CH_2-CH_2-\underset{\underset{CH_3}{|}}{\overset{\overset{CH_3}{|}}{C}}-\underset{O}{\overset{||}{C}}-CH_3$$

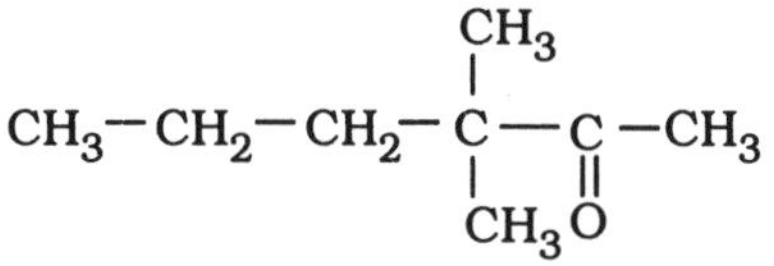

4. a) methanoic acid   b) 3-methylbutanoic acid
   c) 3-methylpentanoic acid

5. a) 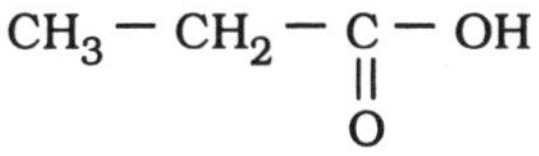
$$CH_3-CH_2-\underset{\overset{||}{O}}{C}-OH \qquad \text{propanoic acid}$$

   b) 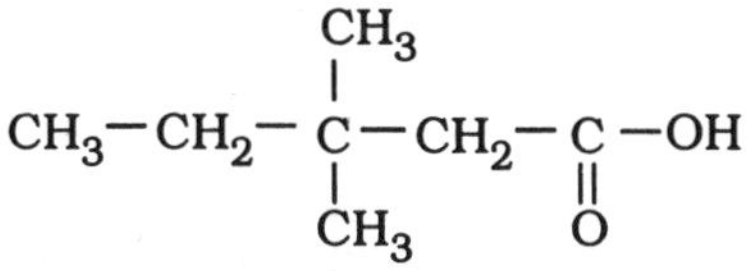
$$CH_3-CH_2-\underset{\underset{CH_3}{|}}{\overset{\overset{CH_3}{|}}{C}}-CH_2-\underset{\overset{||}{O}}{C}-OH \qquad \text{3,3-dimethylpentanoic acid}$$

   c) 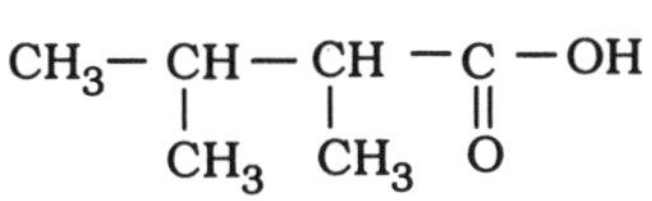
$$CH_3-\underset{\underset{CH_3}{|}}{CH}-\underset{\underset{CH_3}{|}}{CH}-\underset{\overset{||}{O}}{C}-OH \qquad \text{2,3-dimethylbutanoic acid}$$

6. a) 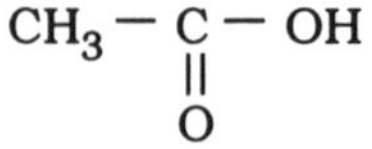 $CH_3 - \underset{\underset{O}{\|}}{C} - OH$

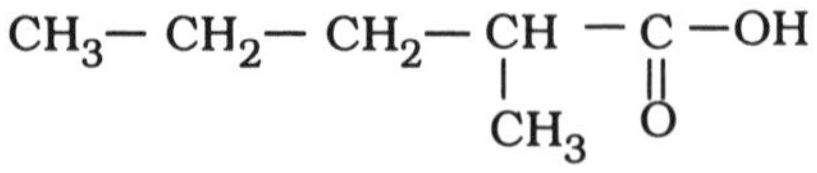

   b) $CH_3 - CH_2 - CH_2 - \underset{\underset{CH_3}{|}}{CH} - \underset{\underset{O}{\|}}{C} - OH$

   c) $CH_3 - CH_2 - \underset{\underset{CH_3}{|}}{\overset{\overset{CH_3}{|}}{C}} - CH_2 - CH_2 - \underset{\underset{O}{\|}}{C} - OH$

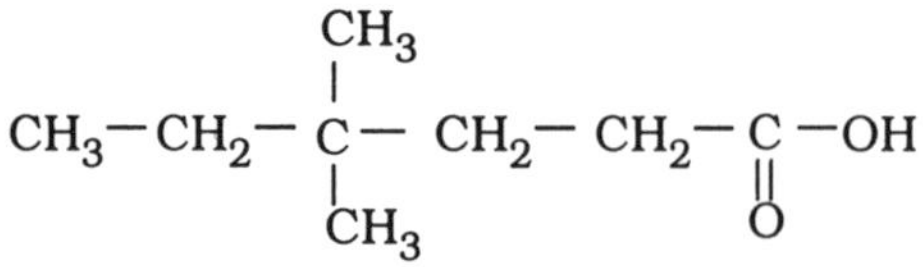

7. a) 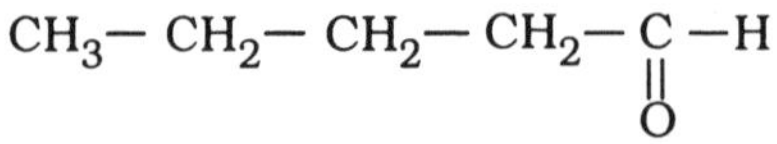 $CH_3 - CH_2 - CH_2 - CH_2 - \underset{\underset{O}{\|}}{C} - H$ **A**

   $CH_3 - CH_2 - \underset{\underset{O}{\|}}{C} - CH_2 - CH_3$ **B**

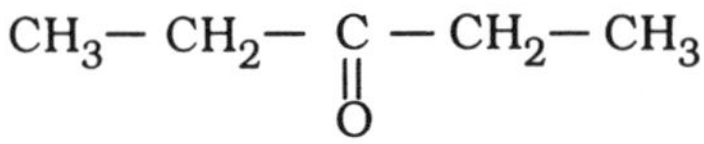

   b) **A** pentanal
   B pentan-3-one

8. a) 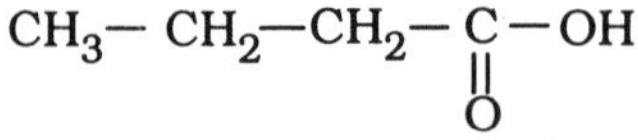 $CH_3 - CH_2 - CH_2 - \underset{\underset{O}{\|}}{C} - OH$ b) 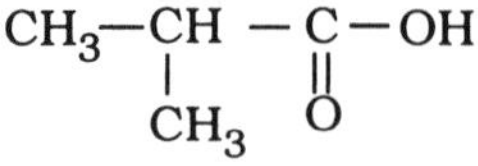 $CH_3 - \underset{\underset{CH_3}{|}}{CH} - \underset{\underset{O}{\|}}{C} - OH$

9. a) 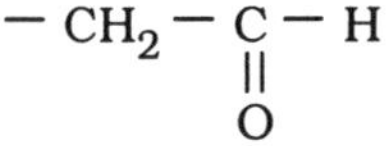 $- CH_2 - \underset{\underset{O}{\|}}{C} - H$

   b) alkanals

   c) i) no
   ii) The only alternative structure is propanone which is an alkanone.

   d) 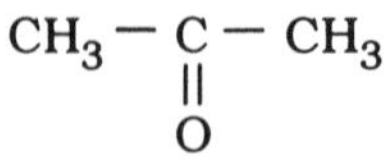 $CH_3 - \underset{\underset{O}{\|}}{C} - CH_3$

   e) alkanones

10. a) alkanals
    b) **X** = methanal   **Y** = ethanal

Exercise 2.5   Nomenclature and structural formulae
- esters

1. a) methyl ethanoate
    b) methyl methanoate
    c) propyl ethanoate
    d) ethyl methanoate

2. a) $CH_3 - \underset{\underset{O}{\|}}{C} - O - CH_2 - CH_3$

    b) $CH_3 - CH_2 - CH_2 - \underset{\underset{O}{\|}}{C} - O - CH_2 - CH_2 - CH_3$

3. a) ethyl methanoate $H - \underset{\underset{O}{\|}}{C} - O - CH_2 - CH_3$

    b) methyl propanoate $CH_3 - CH_2 - \underset{\underset{O}{\|}}{C} - O - CH_3$

    c) ethyl ethanoate $CH_3 - \underset{\underset{O}{\|}}{C} - O - CH_2 - CH_3$

    d) propyl methanoate $H - \underset{\underset{O}{\|}}{C} - O - CH_2 - CH_2 - CH_3$

4. a) ethanol   propanoic acid

        $CH_3 - CH_2 - OH$ $CH_3 - CH_2 - \underset{\underset{O}{\|}}{C} - OH$

    b) methanol   ethanoic acid

        $CH_3 - OH$ $CH_3 - \underset{\underset{O}{\|}}{C} - OH$

    c) ethanol   methanoic acid

        $CH_3 - CH_2 - OH$ $H - \underset{\underset{O}{\|}}{C} - OH$

d) methanol

CH_3-OH

butanoic acid

$CH_3-CH_2-CH_2-\underset{\underset{O}{\|}}{C}-OH$

5. a) methyl methanoate
   b) methanol, methanoic acid (sodium methanoate)

6. a) $CH_3-\underset{\underset{O}{\|}}{C}-O-CH_3$ $H-\underset{\underset{O}{\|}}{C}-O-CH_2-CH_3$

   b) methyl ethanoate   ethyl methanoate

Exercise 2.6   Nomenclature and structural formulae
- aromatic compounds

1. a) benzene
   b) C_6H_6
   c) phenyl

2. Structure **A** implies that benzene contains 3 localised double bonds whilst structure **B** implies that the bonds are delocalised. The molecule does not react with bromine by addition, therefore structure **B** is a better representation.

3.

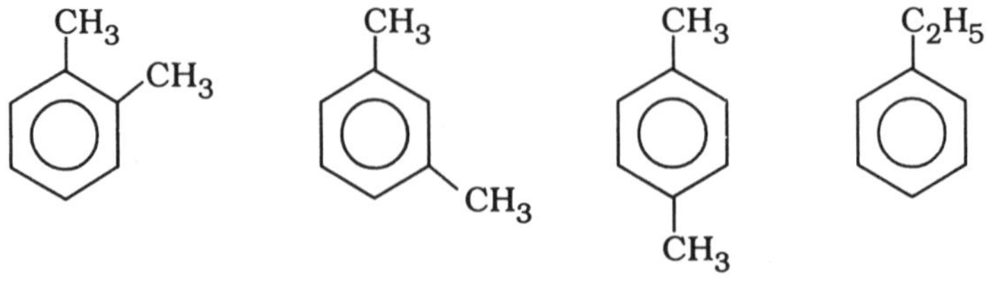

4. aspirin $C_9H_8O_4$ TCP $C_6H_3Cl_3O$ TNT $C_7H_5N_3O_6$

5. The electrons in benzene are delocalised within the molecule but are not free to move from molecule to molecule, hence benzene does not conduct.

   In graphite the electrons are delocalised over an entire plane of carbon atoms and can move throughout he bulk material.

Exercise 2.7   Cracking

1. a) Breaking down a long chain alkane to give a shorter chain alkane and an alkene.

    b)

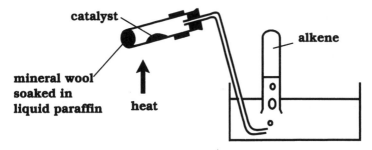

    c) C_2H_4 ethene
    d) Fractions for which demand is low can be converted into more valuable fractions for which demand is high.

2. a) It would reduce the heat energy required.
    b) There are insufficient hydrogen atoms in an alkane to produce two shorter chain alkane molecules.

3. a) chloroethene
    b) **Y** - hydrogen   **Z** - carbon

Exercise 2.8   Addition reactions

1. Add bromine water. If the bromine water is decolourised rapidly, the hydrocarbon is unsatuated.

2. **A** $CH_2=CH-CH_2-CH_2-CH_2-CH_3$

   B

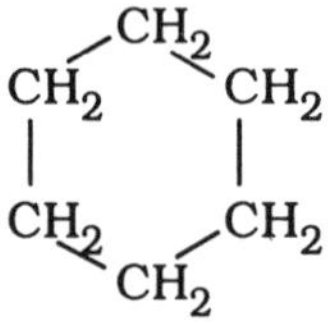

   C $CH_3-CH_2-CH=CH-CH=CH_2$

   D

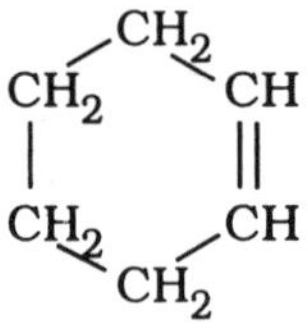

3. a) i)

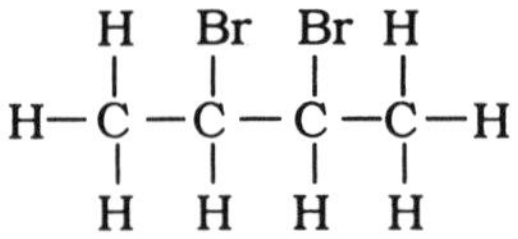

   ii)

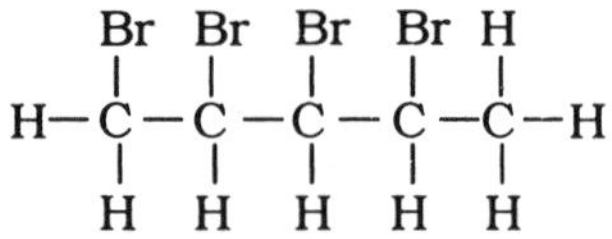

   b) i) 2,3-dibromobutane   ii) 1,2,3,4-tetrabromopentane
   c) addition

4. a)

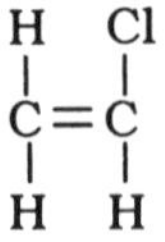

   b) hydrogen chloride

5. a) addition

b) i)
$$
\begin{array}{cc}
\text{H} & \text{Cl} \\
| & | \\
\text{C} & = \text{C} \\
| & | \\
\text{H} & \text{H}
\end{array}
$$

ii)
$$
\begin{array}{cc}
\text{Cl} & \text{Cl} \\
| & | \\
\text{H}-\text{C}-\text{C}-\text{H} \\
| & | \\
\text{H} & \text{H}
\end{array}
$$

iii)
$$
\begin{array}{cc}
\text{H} & \text{Cl} \\
| & | \\
\text{H}-\text{C}-\text{C}-\text{Cl} \\
| & | \\
\text{H} & \text{H}
\end{array}
$$

c) 1,2-dichloroethane

6. a)

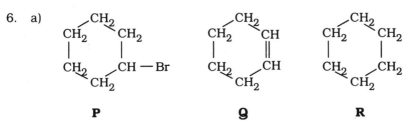

P   Q   R

b) hydrogen bromide

7. a) i) ethene   ii) ethane

b) i)
$$
\begin{array}{cc}
\text{Cl} & \text{Cl} \\
| & | \\
\text{C} & = \text{C} \\
| & | \\
\text{H} & \text{H}
\end{array}
$$

ii)
$$
\begin{array}{cc}
\text{Cl} & \text{Cl} \\
| & | \\
\text{H}-\text{C}-\text{C}-\text{Cl} \\
| & | \\
\text{H} & \text{H}
\end{array}
$$

c) i) hydrogen chloride

ii)
$$
\begin{array}{cc}
\text{H} & \text{Cl} \\
| & | \\
\text{C} & = \text{C} \\
| & | \\
\text{H} & \text{H}
\end{array}
$$

8. a) i)
$$
\begin{array}{cccc}
\text{H}-\text{C}=\text{C}-\text{C}=\text{C}-\text{C}\equiv\text{C}-\text{H} \\
| \quad | \quad | \quad | \\
\text{H} \quad \text{H} \quad \text{H} \quad \text{H}
\end{array}
$$

ii)

$$
\begin{array}{c}
\quad\quad \text{CH}_2 \\
\text{CH} \quad\quad \text{C} \\
\| \quad\quad\quad \| \\
\text{CH} \quad\quad \text{C} \\
\quad\quad \text{CH}_2
\end{array}
$$

b) Add bromine solution to each. Isomers i) and ii) will decolourise bromine solution quickly.

9. a) i) $CH_2=CH-CH_2-CH_3$ $CH_3-CH=CH-CH_3$
      ii) dehydration
   b) i) pentan-1-ol   pentan-3-ol
      ii) pentan-2-ol

10. a) catalytic hydration
   b) fermentation of glucose

11. a) 0.4
   b) cyclohexane
   c) 1.0

Exercise 2.9   Primary, secondary and tertiary alcohols

1. a) primary   b) tertiary   c) secondary
   d) primary   e) primary   f) secondary

2. a) secondary   b) primary   c) primary
   d) secondary   e) tertiary   f) tertiary

3.

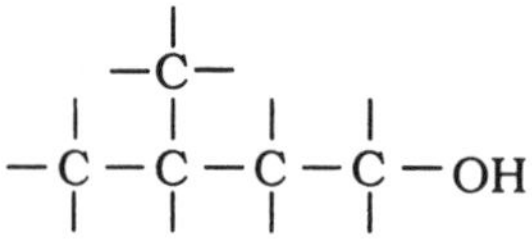

primary 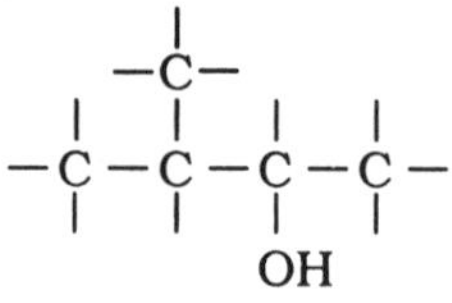   secondary 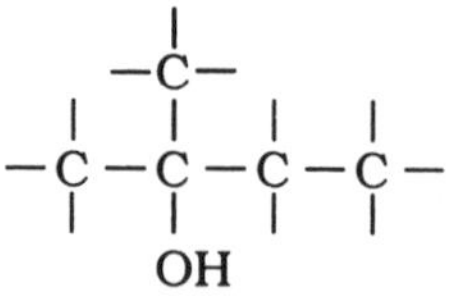   tertiary

Exercise 2.10   Oxidation

1. a) ethanol
   b) $CH_3-\overset{\displaystyle ||}{\underset{\displaystyle O}{C}}-H$
   c) acidified potassium dichromate solution or copper(II) oxide

2. a) $- \underset{\underset{O}{\|}}{C} - H$

   b) $CH_3 - \underset{\underset{CH_3}{|}}{CH} - \underset{\underset{O}{\|}}{C} - H$

   c) $CH_3 - \underset{\underset{O}{\|}}{C} - CH_3$

   d) $CH_3 - CH_2 - \underset{\underset{CH_3}{|}}{CH} - \underset{\underset{O}{\|}}{C} - H$

3. a) $H - \underset{\underset{H}{|}}{\overset{\overset{H}{|}}{C}} - \underset{\underset{H}{|}}{\overset{\overset{H}{|}}{C}} - \underset{\underset{O}{\|}}{C} - H$ $\qquad$ $H - \underset{\underset{H}{|}}{\overset{\overset{H}{|}}{C}} - \underset{\underset{H}{|}}{\overset{\overset{H}{|}}{C}} - \underset{\underset{O}{\|}}{C} - OH$

   b) propan-1-ol $\qquad$ propanoic acid

   c) The orange solution turns green.

4. a) $CH_3 - CH_2 - \underset{\underset{OH}{|}}{CH} - CH_3$ **X** $\qquad$ $CH_3 - CH_2 - \underset{\underset{O}{\|}}{C} - CH_3$ **Y**

   b) butan-2-ol

   c) secondary

5. a) butan-1-ol

   b) propanoic acid

   c) The blue solution gives a brick red precipitate.

6. a) $\overset{\overset{\displaystyle CH_2}{\diagup \quad \diagdown}}{\underset{\underset{\diagdown \quad \diagup}{CH_2}}{\underset{CH_2 \qquad CH_2}{|\qquad\qquad |}}} CH_2 \qquad C = O$

   b) cyclohexanol

7. a) i) $CH_3 - CH_2 - \underset{\underset{OH}{|}}{CH} - CH_3$ ii) $CH_3 - CH_2 - \underset{\underset{O}{\|}}{C} - CH_3$

   b) oxidation

   c) 2-methylpropan-2-ol is a tertiary alcohol and is not easily oxidised.

8. a) 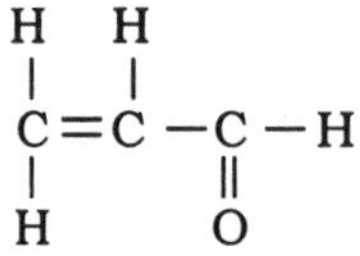
$$
\begin{array}{ccc}
H & H & \\
| & | & \\
C=C & -C & -H \\
| & & \| \\
H & & O
\end{array}
$$

b) Because the molecule gains oxygen.

c) 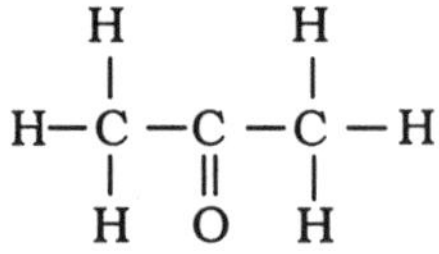
$$
\begin{array}{ccc}
H & & H \\
| & & | \\
H-C & -C & -C -H \\
| & \| & | \\
H & O & H
\end{array}
$$

Exercise 2.11   Making and breaking esters

1. a) ethanoic acid   butan-2-ol

b) Esterification is a reversible reaction; an equilibrium is extablished between reactants and products.

2. a) esterification

b) **X**   ethanoic acid and ethanol

Y   ethyl ethanoate

4. a)

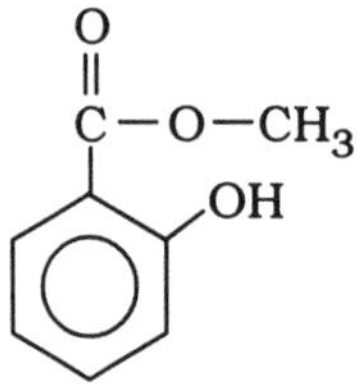

b) i) Breaking down a molecule into two or more smaller molecules by the action of water.

ii) 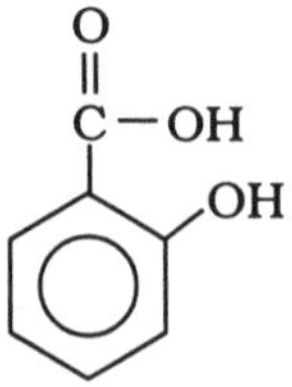
and $CH_3 - C - OH$ with $\|$ O

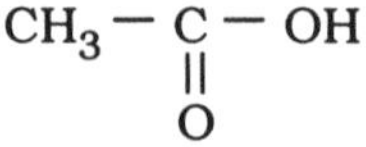

iii) Hydrolysis of aspirin by heat and moisture forms ethanoic acid which smells of vinegar.

5.

$$CH_3-O-\underset{\underset{O}{\|}}{C}-CH-NH-\underset{\underset{O}{\|}}{C}-CH-CH_2-\underset{\underset{O}{\|}}{C}-O-CH_3$$

with CH_2 (attached to benzene ring) on the first CH, and NH_2 on the second CH.

Exercise 2.12 — Percentage yields

1. 80.3%   2. 84.9%   3. 81.6%   4. 88.3%   5. 64.0%

Exercise 2.13 — Uses of carbon compounds

1. a) for example, petrol, kerosine, diesel
   b) for example, plastics, artificial fibres, detergents

2. a) for example, flavourings, solvents
   b) for example, manufacture of esters, solvents

3. a) i) O_3
      ii) It absorbs some of the harmful ultra violet radiation from the sun.
   b) i) The use of chlorofluorocarbons in aerosols and refrigerators.
      ii) For example, increases in the incidence of skin cancers, more rapid melting of polar ice caps.

4. a) for example, aerosol propellants, refrigerants, for foaming plastics
   b) i)
$$Cl-\underset{\underset{F}{|}}{\overset{\overset{F}{|}}{C}}-Cl$$
      ii) 1,2-dichlorotetrafluoroethane

1. a) propane

   b) $C_3H_8 \rightarrow C_3H_6 + H_2$

   c) naphtha

2. a) propene

   b) $CH_2 = CH - CH_3$

   c) 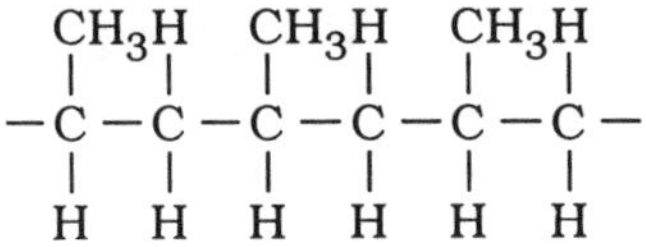
   $$\begin{array}{cccccc} CH_3H & CH_3H & CH_3H \\ | \ | & | \ | & | \ | \\ -C-C-C-C-C-C- \\ | \ | & | \ | & | \ | \\ H \ \ H & H \ \ H & H \ \ H \end{array}$$

3. a) 4

   b) 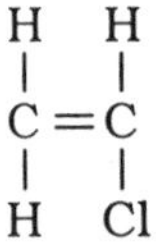
   $$\begin{array}{cc} H & H \\ | & | \\ C & = & C \\ | & | \\ H & Cl \end{array}$$

   c) addition

4. a) poly(tetrafluoroethene)

   b) 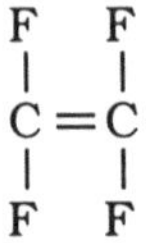
   $$\begin{array}{cc} F & F \\ | & | \\ C & = & C \\ | & | \\ F & F \end{array}$$

   c)
   $$\begin{array}{cccccc} F & F & F & F & F & F \\ | & | & | & | & | & | \\ -C-C-C-C-C-C- \\ | & | & | & | & | & | \\ F & F & F & F & F & F \end{array}$$

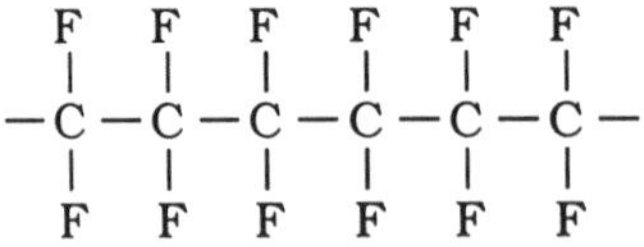

5. a) 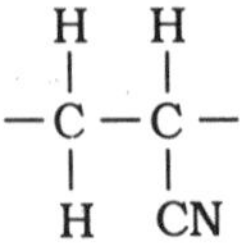
   $$\begin{array}{cc} H & H \\ | & | \\ -C-C- \\ | & | \\ H & CN \end{array}$$

   b) 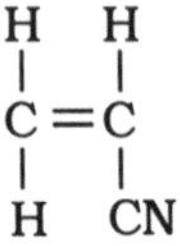
   $$\begin{array}{cc} H & H \\ | & | \\ C & = & C \\ | & | \\ H & CN \end{array}$$

   c) addition polymerisation

6. a) Styrene would decolourise bromine solution rapidly.

   b) styrene

   c) addition

   d)

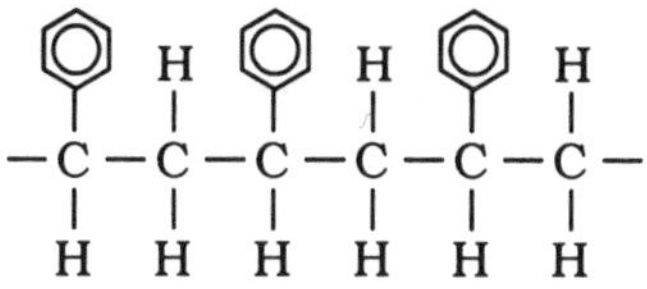

7. a)

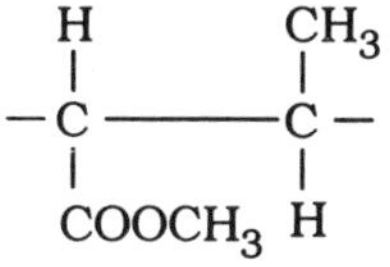

   b)

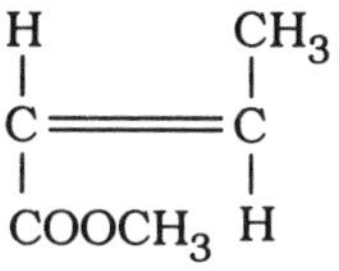

   c) addition

8. a)

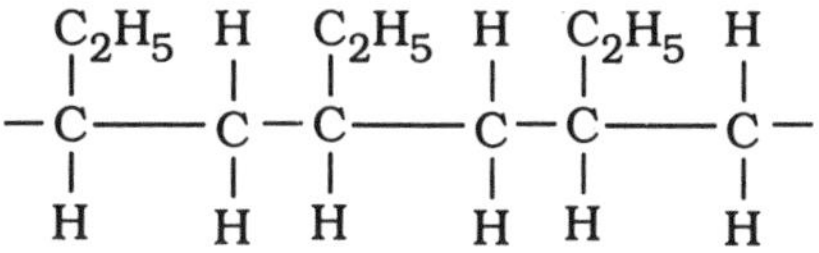

   b) addition

   c) i)

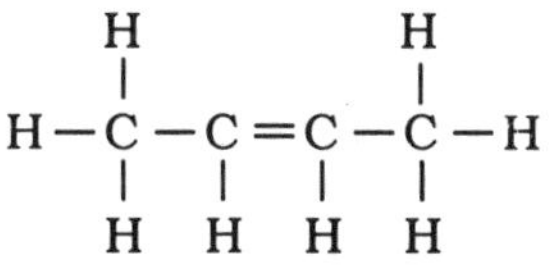

      ii)

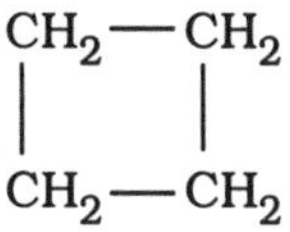

9. a)

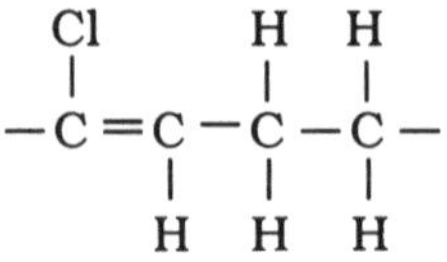

$$-\overset{\underset{\displaystyle |}{Cl}}{C}=\overset{\underset{\displaystyle |}{H}}{C}-\overset{\underset{\displaystyle |}{H}}{\underset{\displaystyle H}{C}}-\overset{\underset{\displaystyle |}{H}}{\underset{\displaystyle H}{C}}-$$

b) This polymer would rapidly decolourise bromine solution. Poly(ethene) would not.

10. a) addition

b)

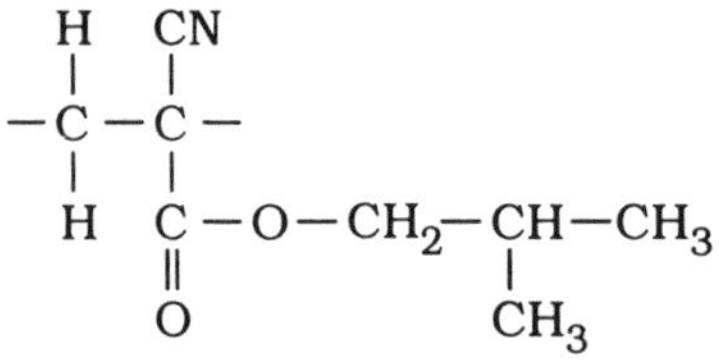

$$-\overset{\underset{\displaystyle |}{H}}{\underset{\displaystyle H}{C}}-\overset{\underset{\displaystyle |}{CN}}{\underset{\displaystyle \underset{\displaystyle O}{C-O-CH_2-CH-CH_3}}{C}}-$$
(with CH_3 below CH)

Exercise 2.15   Early plastics and fibres (ii)

1.* a) 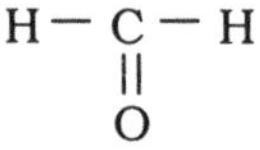 $H-\overset{\displaystyle C}{\underset{\displaystyle \|\ O}{|}}-H$

2. a) natural gas   b) water
   c) hydrogen and carbon monoxide   d) oxidation
   e) manufacture of thermosetting plastic, eg. urea-methanol resin

3. a) synthesis gas   b)

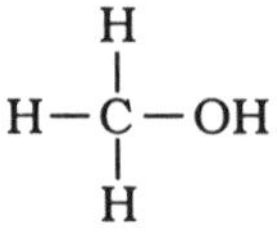

   $$H-\overset{\underset{\displaystyle |}{H}}{\underset{\displaystyle H}{C}}-OH$$

   c) methanal
   d) It is cross linked and forms a rigid three-dimensional structure.

4. a) **A** - a diamine   **B** - a dicarboxylic acid
   b) condensation
   c)

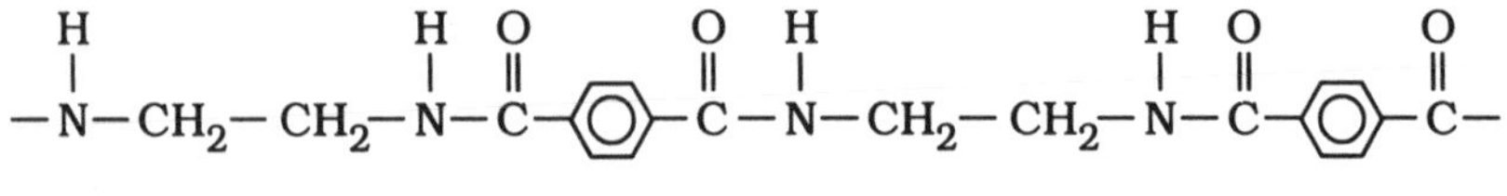

   $$-\overset{\underset{|}{H}}{N}-CH_2-CH_2-\overset{\underset{|}{H}}{N}-\overset{\overset{O}{\|}}{C}-\bigcirc\!\!\!\!\bigcirc-\overset{\overset{O}{\|}}{C}-\overset{\underset{|}{H}}{N}-CH_2-CH_2-\overset{\underset{|}{H}}{N}-\overset{\overset{O}{\|}}{C}-\bigcirc\!\!\!\!\bigcirc-\overset{\overset{O}{\|}}{C}-$$

5. a) water

b)

$$-O-\overset{\overset{\displaystyle H}{|}}{\underset{\underset{\displaystyle H}{|}}{C}}-\overset{\overset{\displaystyle H}{|}}{\underset{\underset{\displaystyle H}{|}}{C}}-O-\overset{\overset{\displaystyle O}{||}}{C}\overset{}{\bigcirc}\overset{\overset{\displaystyle O}{||}}{C}-O-\overset{\overset{\displaystyle H}{|}}{\underset{\underset{\displaystyle H}{|}}{C}}-\overset{\overset{\displaystyle H}{|}}{\underset{\underset{\displaystyle H}{|}}{C}}-O-\overset{\overset{\displaystyle O}{||}}{C}\overset{}{\bigcirc}\overset{\overset{\displaystyle O}{||}}{C}-$$

c) for example, nylon

6. a) i)

$$H-\overset{\overset{\displaystyle H}{|}}{N}- CH_2- CH_2- CH_2- CH_2- CH_2 - \overset{\overset{\displaystyle O}{||}}{C}-OH$$

   ii)

$$-\overset{\overset{\displaystyle H}{|}}{N}- (CH_2)_5 - \overset{\overset{\displaystyle O}{||}}{C}-$$

b) i)

$$-\overset{\overset{\displaystyle H}{|}}{N}-(CH_2)_6 -\overset{\overset{\displaystyle H}{|}}{N}-\overset{\overset{\displaystyle O}{||}}{C}-(CH_2)_4 -\overset{\overset{\displaystyle O}{||}}{C}-$$

   ii)

$$H-\overset{\overset{\displaystyle H}{|}}{N}-(CH_2)_6 -\overset{\overset{\displaystyle H}{|}}{N}-H \qquad HO-\overset{\overset{\displaystyle O}{||}}{C}-(CH_2)_4 -\overset{\overset{\displaystyle O}{||}}{C}-OH$$

   iii) polyamide

c) Nylon molecules are held together by strong hydrogen bonds.

7. a)

$$-O-\overset{\overset{\displaystyle H}{|}}{\underset{\underset{\displaystyle H}{|}}{C}}-\overset{\overset{\displaystyle H}{|}}{\underset{\underset{\displaystyle H}{|}}{C}}-O-\overset{\overset{\displaystyle O}{||}}{C}-\bigcirc-\overset{\overset{\displaystyle O}{||}}{C}-$$

b)

$$HO-\overset{\overset{\displaystyle H}{|}}{\underset{\underset{\displaystyle H}{|}}{C}}-\overset{\overset{\displaystyle H}{|}}{\underset{\underset{\displaystyle H}{|}}{C}}-OH \qquad HO-\overset{\overset{\displaystyle O}{||}}{C}-\bigcirc-\overset{\overset{\displaystyle O}{||}}{C}-OH$$

c) condensation polymer

8. a) linear polymers - for example, synthetic fibres

   three dimensional polymers - for example, electrical fittings

   b) i)

$$-O-(CH_2)_2-O-\overset{\overset{\displaystyle O}{\|}}{C}-(CH_2)_4-\overset{\overset{\displaystyle O}{\|}}{C}-O-(CH_2)_2-O-\overset{\overset{\displaystyle O}{\|}}{C}-(CH_2)_4-\overset{\overset{\displaystyle O}{\|}}{C}-$$

   ii) condensation polymerisation

   iii) The carbon chain is saturated and there is no third functional group in either monomer which would allow chains to cross link.

9. a) It has a linear structure and cannot cross link.

   b)

$$HO-\overset{\overset{\displaystyle CH_3}{|}}{\underset{\underset{\displaystyle H}{|}}{C}}-CH_2-\overset{\overset{\displaystyle O}{\|}}{C}-OH \qquad HO-\overset{\overset{\displaystyle C_2H_5}{|}}{\underset{\underset{\displaystyle H}{|}}{C}}-CH_2-\overset{\overset{\displaystyle O}{\|}}{C}-OH$$

Exercise 2.16   Recent developments

1. a) synthetic, polyamide

   b) The structure is held together by strong covalent bonds and adjacent fibres are held together by extensive hydrogen bonds forming very strong sheets of polymer.

   c) for example, bullet proof vests, aerospace components

2. a) poly(ethyne)

   b) $H-C \equiv C-H$

   c) i) The electrons in the double bonds of the polymer chain can delocalise.

   ii) For example, the membrane for high-performance loud speakers.

3. a) It becomes electrically conducting when exposed to light.

   b) Manufacture of photo-conducting drums in photocopiers.

4. a) i) addition polymerisation

   ii) hydrolysis

   b) for example, hospital laundry bags

   c) The polymer molecule contains many -OH groups which can hydrogen bond to water molecules making the polymer soluble.

5. a) i) A polymer which can be broken down by the action of bacteria in soil.

   ii) A polymer which can be broken down by exposure to light.

   b) Biodegradable polymers - for example, polylactic acid, polyvinyl alcohol.
   Photodegradable polymers - for example, low density poly(ethene) with carbonyl groups incorporated into the carbon skeleton.

   c) Plastic waste which is either biodegradable or photodegradable will break down and will have a limited lifetime in the environment, unlike conventional polymers which create litter and waste problems for many years.

Exercise 2.17   Fats and oils

1. a) They provide an efficient means by which the body can store energy.

   b) The long saturated hydrocarbon chains in fats can twist into a relatively small volume, whereas the presence of the double bond in the hydrocarbon chains of an oil restricts this. The fat molecules are much more compact and larger van der Waals' forces can exist between fat molecules giving rise to melting points above room temperature. The smaller van der Waals' forces in oils give a lower melting point, below room temperature.

2. a)

   b) The melting point is increased.   c) (catalytic) hydrogenation

3. a)

$$H-\overset{\displaystyle \overset{H}{|}}{\underset{\displaystyle \underset{OH}{|}}{C}}-\overset{\displaystyle \overset{H}{|}}{\underset{\displaystyle \underset{OH}{|}}{C}}-\overset{\displaystyle \overset{H}{|}}{\underset{\displaystyle \underset{OH}{|}}{C}}-H$$

b) 1:3

4. a) esters

b)

$$CH_2-O-\overset{\displaystyle \overset{O}{\|}}{C}-(CH_2)_{14}-CH_3$$
$$CH_2-O-\overset{\displaystyle \overset{O}{\|}}{C}-(CH_2)_{14}-CH_3$$
$$CH_2-O-\overset{\displaystyle \overset{O}{\|}}{C}-(CH_2)_{14}-CH_3$$

c) It is likely to be a fat because the carbon chains are saturated.

5. a) (enzyme) hydrolysis
   b) i) saturated
      ii) glycerol (propan-1,2,3-triol)

6. a) (alkaline) hydrolysis
   b) A soap molecule consists of a long hydrocarbon "tail" which is soluble in grease (hydrophobic) and an ionic head which is water soluble (hydrophilic).

Exercise 2.18   Proteins

1. a) Proteins are essential for the growth and repair of tissue.
   b) amino acids
   c) carbon, hydrogen, oxygen and nitrogen

2. a)

$$-\overset{\displaystyle \overset{H}{|}}{N}-CH_2-\overset{\displaystyle \overset{O}{\|}}{C}-\overset{\displaystyle \overset{H}{|}}{N}-CH_2-\overset{\displaystyle \overset{O}{\|}}{C}-\overset{\displaystyle \overset{H}{|}}{N}-CH_2-\overset{\displaystyle \overset{O}{\|}}{C}-$$

   b) condensation polymerisation
   c) essential amino acids

3. a)

$$-\overset{\overset{\displaystyle O}{\|}}{C}-\overset{\overset{\displaystyle H}{|}}{N}-$$

b) i) 2

ii)

$$H-\overset{\overset{\displaystyle H}{|}}{N}-CH_2-\overset{\overset{\displaystyle O}{\|}}{C}-OH$$ $$H-\overset{\overset{\displaystyle H}{|}}{N}-\overset{\overset{\displaystyle CH_3}{|}}{CH}-\overset{\overset{\displaystyle O}{\|}}{C}-OH$$

iii) hydrolysis

4. a) proteins

b)

   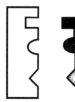

Substrate molecules adsorb onto the surface of the catalyst by a lock and key mechanism.

Reaction takes place at lower activation energy and the product desorbs from the catalyst surface.

5. a)

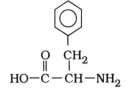

$$HO-\overset{\overset{\displaystyle O}{\|}}{C}-\overset{\overset{\displaystyle CH_2}{|}}{CH}-NH_2$$

$$HO-\overset{\overset{\displaystyle O}{\|}}{C}-\overset{\overset{\displaystyle }{\underset{\underset{\displaystyle NH_2}{|}}{CH}}}-CH_2-\overset{\overset{\displaystyle O}{\|}}{C}-OH$$

b) Cooking would hydrolyse aspartame and its sweetness would be lost. In cold drinks, hydrolysis is very slow, an aspartame remains unchanged.

6. a) The sucrose molecule is not the correct shape to fit the active site of maltase.

b) The change of pH causes the protein molecule to denature and the maltose molecule can no longer fit into the active site of the enzyme.

c) temperature

1. a) cracking
   b) fractional distillation
   c) addition polymerisation

2. **A** $CH_2 = CH_2$
   B $\begin{array}{c} CH_3-CH_2 \\ \\ CH_3-CH_2 \end{array}\!\!\!\!\begin{array}{c} \\ C=O \\ \\ \end{array}$

   C $\begin{array}{c} \\ CH_3CH_2-C \\ \\ \end{array}\!\!\!\!\begin{array}{c} O \\ \diagup\diagup \\ \diagdown \\ OH \end{array}$

3. a)

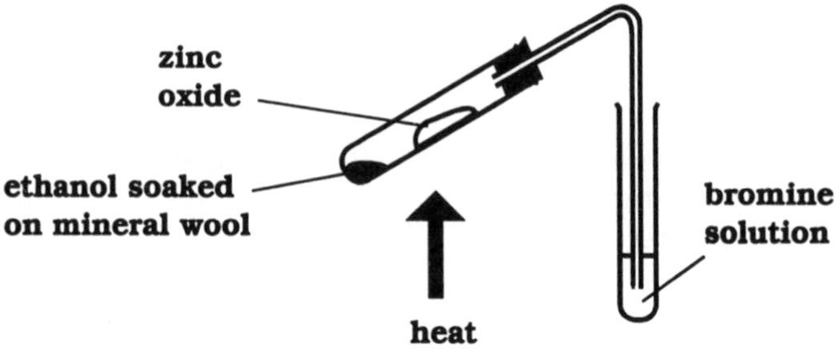

   b) If the product decolourises bromine solution, dehydration has occurred. If dehydrogenation has occurred, the bromine solution will remain brown.

4. a) $\underset{\underset{CH_3}{|}}{CH_2{=}CH{-}CH{-}CH_3}$ b) an alkanone

   c) i) heated aluminium oxide

   ii) $\underset{\underset{CH_3}{|}}{CH_3{-}CH{=}C{-}CH_3}$

   d) $\underset{\underset{CH_3}{|}}{CH_2Cl{-}CHCl{-}CH{-}CH_3}$

5. a) **A**

$$H_2C=CH_2$$

(structure: $C=C$ with H, H on left carbon and H, H on right carbon)

B

(structure: $H-\overset{\displaystyle H}{\underset{\displaystyle H}{C}}-\overset{\displaystyle H}{C}=O$)

C

(structure: $H-\overset{\displaystyle H}{\underset{\displaystyle H}{C}}-C\overset{\displaystyle OH}{\underset{\displaystyle O}{}}$)

b) 1   hydrogen bromide

    2   hydrogen (using a nickel catalyst)

    3   acidified potassium dichromate solution or copper(II) oxide

6. a) i)   It does not contain a carbon to carbon double bond.

     ii)   It is a ketone

  b)   propanone

(structure: $H-\overset{\displaystyle H}{\underset{\displaystyle H}{C}}-\overset{}{\underset{\displaystyle O}{C}}-\overset{\displaystyle H}{\underset{\displaystyle H}{C}}-H$, middle carbon double bonded to O)

7.

$$CH_3-CH=CH_2 \quad \underset{H_2SO_4 \text{ catalyst}}{\overset{H_2O}{\rightarrow}} \quad CH_3-\underset{OH}{CH}-CH_3$$

↓ acidified potassium dichromate solution

$$CH_3-\underset{O}{\overset{\|}{C}}-CH_3$$

8. **A**   fractional distillation   **B**   reforming

   C   cracking   **D**   (catalytic) hydration

   E   addition polymerisation   **F**   oxidation

   G   condensation

9. a) **A** $CH_3-CH=CH_2$ **C** $CH_3-\underset{OH}{CH}-CH_3$ **D** $CH_3-\underset{O}{\overset{\|}{C}}-CH_3$

  b) 1   addition   2   oxidation

10. a) i) CH$_3$—CH—C—H
          | ||
         CH$_3$ O

     ii) CH$_3$—CH$_2$—C—CH$_3$
                  ||
                  O

  b) **A** butanal   **B** butanoic acid

  c) **C** will decolourise bromine solution rapidly in the dark. **A** will not.

  d) i) acidified potassium dichromate solution or copper(II) oxide

     ii) hot aluminium oxide

  e) i) poly(but-1-ene)

     ii)

       C$_2$H$_5$ H   C$_2$H$_5$ H   C$_2$H$_5$ H
         | | | | | |
    —C———C—C———C—C———C—
        | | | | | |
       H   H H   H   H   H

11. a) **P** propan-1-ol   **Q** propan-2-ol

  b) **1** catalytic dehydration   **2** oxidation

  c) CH$_3$—CH$_2$—C—H
                ||
                O

  d) -NH$_2$ amine group   —C—OH carboxyl group
                             ||
                             O

12. a) carbon-carbon double bond

  b)
            H H
           | |
   ⟨O⟩—C=C—CH$_3$

  c) aromatic,   aldehyde

  d) Benedict's solution or acidified potassium dichromate solution

  e) CH$_3$—C=O
            |
            H

13. a) i) **I** butan-1-ol   **II** butan-2-ol
        III methylpropan-2-ol   **IV** methylpropan-1-ol

     ii) **I** and **IV** primary   **II** secondary   **III** tertiary

b)   i) **D** must be compound III because it is tertiary and cannot be oxidised.

ii) **C** must be compound II because it cannot be oxidised to an acid.

iii) If **D** is III and dehydrates to the same alkene as **A**, **A** must have a branched chain and is therefore IV. By elimination **B** is I. It can give the same alkene as **C** on dehydration.

14. a) $CH_2 = CH - CH_2 - CH_3$ $CH_2 = \underset{\underset{CH_3}{|}}{C} - CH_3$

$CH_3 - CH = CH - CH_3$

b)   i) a brick red precipitate

ii) **Y** is an alkanal.   **Z** is an alkanone.

iii) the branched chain alkene

iv) methylpropene

c)   i) $\begin{array}{c} CH_2 - CH_2 \\ |\qquad\ | \\ CH_2 - CH_2 \end{array}$

ii) cyclobutane

iii) Test with bromine solution. Cyclobutane would **not** decolourise bromine solution quickly.

15. a)   cracking of ethane or naphtha

b) **W** 1,2 dichloroethane   **X** water

c) **Y**

$$H-\underset{\underset{H}{|}}{\overset{\overset{H}{|}}{C}}-\underset{\underset{H}{|}}{\overset{\overset{H}{|}}{C}}-Cl$$

Z

$$H-\underset{\underset{H}{|}}{\overset{\overset{H}{|}}{C}}-\underset{\underset{O}{||}}{C}-H$$

d)   i) addition polymerisation

ii)

e) i) condensation polymerisation
   ii) ethan-1,2-diol

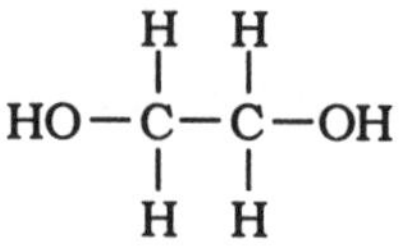

$$HO-\overset{\overset{\displaystyle H}{|}}{\underset{\underset{\displaystyle H}{|}}{C}}-\overset{\overset{\displaystyle H}{|}}{\underset{\underset{\displaystyle H}{|}}{C}}-OH$$

   terephthalic acid

$$HO-\overset{\overset{\displaystyle O}{\|}}{C}-\langle \bigcirc \rangle-\overset{\overset{\displaystyle O}{\|}}{C}-OH$$

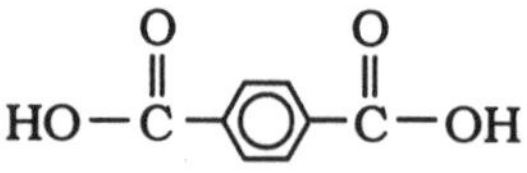

16. a) secondary alcohol
    b) 3 $CH_2{=}CH{-}CH_2{-}CH_3$
       2 $CH_3{-}CH{=}CH{-}CH_3$
    c) **A** hot aluminium oxide
       B hydrogen bromide
       D acidified potassium dichromate solution or copper(II) oxide
       E Benedict's solution or acidified potassium dichromate solution
    d) 8 $CH_3-CH_2-\overset{\overset{\displaystyle }{\underset{\underset{\displaystyle O}{\|}}{C}}-CH_3$

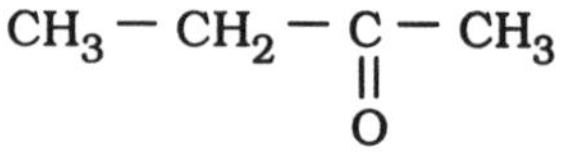

       9 $CH_3-CH_2-CH_2-\overset{}{\underset{\underset{\displaystyle H}{|}}{C}}{=}O$

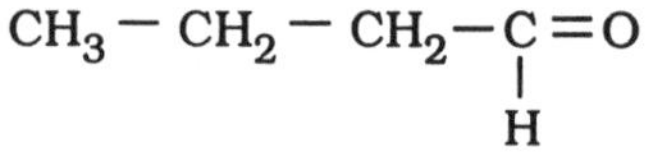

    e) 7

Unit 3   Chemical Reactions

Exercise 3.1   The chemical industry

1. The income to the UK economy from goods manufactured by the chemical industry and sold to other countries is greater than the expenditure of UK companies on chemical products manufactured abroad.

2. a) Research is the process of investigating procedures for the synthesis of new materials or for improvements in the means of synthesising existing materials.

    b) A pilot study is an investigation which attempts to produce materials on a scale larger than the small scale procedures developed during initial research.

    c) Scaling up is the process where the results of the pilot study are used to develop a manufacturing process on a scale large enough to meet consumer demand at an effective cost.

    d) Production is the on-going process of manufacturing consumer products or feedstocks in the most cost effective way.

    e) Review is the analysis of production methods to ensure that they are as efficient as possible and minimise possible harmful effects on the environment and wellbeing of plant operators.

3. For example:
    Manufacture of sulphuric acid (Contact process)
    Sulphur is burned in dry air to form sulphur dioxide.
    Sulphur dioxide is mixed with oxygen and passed into a catalyst chamber at a temperature of 450 °C. In the presence of vanadium(V) oxide, sulphur trioxide forms. The sulphur trioxide is dissolved in concentrated sulphuric acid to form oleum, which is then diluted with water to form sulphuric acid.
    Manufacture of ammonia (Haber process)
    Nitrogen, produced by the fractional distillation of liquid air, is mixed with hydrogen, produced by treating methane with steam, and passed over iron at a temperature of 450 °C under high pressure. The resulting gases are cooled and liquid ammonia is produced. Unused nitrogen and hydrogen are recycled.

4. a) A feedstock is a substance produced from raw materials which can be further processed into consumer products.

    b) cost

5. a) A raw material is a naturally occurring substance which can be converted into feedstocks or directly into consumer products.

    b) air, water, oil, coal, iron ore, natural gas, aluminium oxide

6. For example, by the use of catalysts which allow reactions to occur at lower temperatures, by using the energy produced in an exothermic reaction as a source of heat.

7. a) A batch process is normally used when relatively small quantities of materials such as dyes and pharmaceuticals are to be produced. The apparatus is charged with its feedstocks, and when the reaction is complete, the apparatus is emptied, cleaned and refilled with a fresh charge of feedstock.
        A continuous process has a continuous input of feedstocks and makes products on a round the clock basis without interruption.

    b) For example, batch processes are useful where small quantities of product are required. The process can be operated on demand and the apparatus may be suitable for a number of similar reactions.
        For example, a continuous process is dedicated to the production of a single product on a very large scale. It can be operated under computer control and usually requires a small workforce. It can be designed to operate at maximum efficiency, since there is no need to stop production.

    c) batch process - for example, dyes, pharmaceuticals
        continuous process - for example, sulphuric acid, ammonia

8. a) For example, improvements in safety procedures such as provision of specialised clothing, provision of specialised fire-fighting services on site.

    b) For example, constant monitoring of air and water to ensure that there are no discharges into the environment above accepted safety levels, warning systems to alert local residents of possible dangers.

9. a) For example, reduced discharge of potentially harmful chemicals into rivers, processing of exhaust gases to reduce the discharge of pollutants such as sulphur dioxide into the environment.

10. For example:
    Nearby supplies of raw materials to supply the plant,
    availability of a convenient means of transport of products from the plant,
    availability of a suitable pool of skilled labour,
    availability of a cheap and reliable source of energy.

11. a) Capital costs are the costs of building the plant and its associated infrastructure.
        Fixed costs are those incurred regardless of whether the plant is fully operational or only operating at part of its capacity.
        Variable costs are those costs determined by the output of the plant.

    b) For example:

        Capital costs   -   cost of plant construction
                             cost of purchase of construction site
        Fixed costs   -   repayments of loan capital
                             employees salaries
        Variable costs   -   cost of raw materials
                             cost of distribution of products

12. a) A capital intensive process is one where the major expenditure in operating the plant involves the cost of building the facility. A labour intensive industry is one where the major cost is in payments to workers in the industry.

    b) The sales income for a capital intensive industry per employee is very large, whereas for a labour intensive industry it is much smaller.

13. The cost of building the plant to specifications suitable for operating at 400 atmospheres pressure would be very much greater than if the plant were to operate at 200 atmospheres. Reactor vessels would have to be much stronger and require greater quantities of material, and pumps would have to be much larger and much more expensive to purchase and operate.

14. a) Nitrogen from air can be obtained very cheaply.
        Natural gas is a cheap and plentiful raw material from which to produce hydrogen.
        Unreacted gases can be recycled avoiding any wastage.

    b) Ethene, the feedstock for many plastics, is produced from either the cracking of ethane from natural gas, or form the cracking of the naphtha fraction of crude oil. The latter is a more expensive source of ethene. However, where a refinery produces more naphtha than is needed for the production of petrol additives, the excess can be used to produce ethene economically.

Exercise 3.2   Hess's Law

1. a) **c = b - a**
   b) The enthalpy change of a chemical reaction is the same irrespective of
       the number of steps required to achieve that change.

2. $\Delta H = -2249$ kJ mol^{-1} 3. $\Delta H = +682$ kJ mol^{-1}

4. $\Delta H = -39.2$ kJ mol^{-1} 5. $\Delta H = -286$ kJ mol^{-1}

6. $\Delta H = -132$ kJ mol^{-1} 7. $\Delta H = -91$ kJ mol^{-1}

8. $\Delta H = -316$ kJ mol^{-1} 9. $\Delta H = -86$ kJ mol^{-1}

10. $\Delta H = -160$ kJ mol^{-1} 11. $\Delta H = -2881$ kJ mol^{-1}

12. $\Delta H = -275$ kJ mol^{-1} 13. $\Delta H = +53$ kJ mol^{-1}

14. $\Delta H = -2051$ kJ mol^{-1}

Exercise 3.3   Equilibrium

1. a) Equilibrium will move to the right.
   b) Equilibrium will move to the right.

2. a) The brown colour will fade.
   b) The brown colour will become more intense.
   c) The brown colour will become more intense.
   d) No visible change.

3. a) The equilibrium will move to the right.
   b) The equilibrium will move to the left.
   c) The equilibrium will move to the left.

4. a) The brown colour will fade and become more yellow because the equilibrium will move in its exothermic direction.

   b) The brown colour will fade and become more yellow because the equilibrium will move in the direction which produces a smaller number of molecules.

5. a) The forward reaction is endothermic.

   b) The equilibrium will move to the left if the pressure is increased. The formation of methane and steam reduces the number of molecules in the equilibrium mixture, which will oppose the applied increase in pressure.

   c) i) The rate of formation of synthesis gas will increase.

      ii) The composition of the equilibrium mixture will be unchanged.

6. a) i) The equilibrium will move to oppose the decrease in temperature so the reaction proceeds in its exothermic direction.

      ii) If the pressure is increased, the equilibrium will move to oppose the change and reduce the overall number of molecules, i.e. will move in its forward direction.

   b) i) If the temperature is reduced below 300 °C, the reaction will be too slow to be economical.

      ii) The use of pressures greater than 70 atmospheres will require much more expensive plant and pumping equipment. The improvement in yield would not justify the additional capital cost.

7. a) The equilibrium will move to the left.

   b) The equilibrium will move to the right.

   c) The equilibrium will move to the right.

8. a) Reaction (1)   ii)

      Reaction (2)   iii)

      Reaction (3)   i)

      Reaction (4)   i)

   b) The equilibrium will move to the left.

9. a) hydrogen chloride

   b) The increase in concentration of hydrogen chloride drives the equilibrium to the left and reduces the concentration of magnesium oxide which would form.

10. a) High pressure will cause the equilibrium in reaction **A** to move to the right, but the equilibrium would move to the left in reaction **B**.

   b) Since each reaction is exothermic, high temperatures will move the equilibria to the left, decreasing the yield. The higher temperature for reaction **B** is consistent with the need to reach equilibrium quickly but is not favourable in terms of yield.

11. a) Bleaching efficiency would be reduced.
    b) Bleaching efficiency would be reduced.
    c) no effect
    d) Bleaching efficiency would be increased.

12. a) At equilibrium, equal numbers of iodine molecules move from the KI solution through the interface into the chloroform as move in the opposite direction.

   b) When more chloroform is added, the iodine solution is diluted. The number of molecules of iodine passing through the interface from the chloroform to the KI solution is reduced. There will be a net transfer of iodine molecules from the KI solution into the chloroform until equilibrium is re-established.

13. a) The addition of dilute sulphuric acid would move the equilibrium to the left and more calcium sulphate would precipitate out.

   b) Addition of barium chloride would cause the sulphate ion to precipitate out as barium sulphate. The equilibrium would move to the right and more calcium sulphate would dissolve.

14.*a) Increasing temperature would cause both processes to move in their endothermic direction to oppose the applied change. The equilibria would both move to the left.

   b) At atmospheric pressure the equilibrium position of the Contact process is sufficiently far to the right to make the process economical. Increasing the pressure would increase capital costs by more than is commercially justified.
   In the Haber process, the yield of ammonia at atmospheric pressure is very low and the increased yield at 200 atmospheres justifies the additional capital cost.

c) Increasing the pressure beyond 200 atmospheres in the Haber process will increase the yield of ammonia. There will be increased capital cost involved in using heavier walled pressure vessels and pumping machinery which will make the higher pressure process less economical.

15. a) The use of higher pressure will move the equilibrium to the right and increase the yield of methanol.

  b) i) exothermic

   ii) Since the yield is lower at 500 °C than at 300 °C the equilibrium has moved to the left at higher temperatures. The reaction must therefore be endothermic in the direction which decreases the yield.

16. a) The colour would intensify since the addition of $H^+(aq)$ will drive the equilibrium to the left.

  b) Silver nitrate will remove $Br^-(aq)$ from the equilibrium mixture as $AgBr(s)$. The equilibrium will move to the right and the brown colour will decrease in intensity.

17. a) 600 atmospheres, 200 °C

  b) i) Since the number of molecules on the left hand side of the equation is greater than the number of molecules on the right, increase of pressure will drive the equilibrium to the right and give higher yields.

   ii) The reaction is exothermic in the forward direction. Increase in temperature will cause the equilibrium to move in its endothermic direction and decrease the yield.

  c) A temperature of 400 °C is the best compromise to obtain adequate yield and a fast enough reaction. 200 atmospheres pressure is used since it is not commercially justified to incur increased capital costs in installing plant designed to operate at higher pressures.

Exercise 3.4   The pH scale

1. a) 10^{-7} mol l^{-1}
    b) The concentrations of the OH$^-$(aq) ions and H$^+$(aq) ions are the same.

2. a) 3   b) 9   c) 0   d) 13

3. a) 1×10^{-11} mol l^{-1} b) 1 mol l^{-1} c) 1×10^{-8} mol l^{-1} d) 10 mol l^{-1}

4. a) 1×10^{-12} mol l^{-1} b) 1×10^{-13} mol l^{-1}
    c) 1×10^{-8} mol l^{-1} d) 1×10^{-7} mol l^{-1}

5. a) 1×10^{-12} mol l^{-1} b) 1×10^{-7} mol l^{-1}
    c) 1×10^{-14} mol l^{-1} d) 1 mol l^{-1}

Exercise 3.5   Strong and weak acids and bases

1. a) i)   A concentrated acid contains a large quantity of pure acid
             dissolved to make a relatively small volume of solution.
             A dilute acid contains a small quantity of pure acid dissolved to
             make a relatively large volume of solution.
        ii) A weak acid contains a large proportion of unionised molecules of
             acid in aqueous solution.
             A strong acid is almost fully ionised in solution.
    b) i)   for example, ethanoic acid, citric acid
        ii) for example, hydrochloric acid, sulphuric acid, nitric acid
    c) i)   The concentration of hydrogen ions decreases in proportion to
             the volume of the acid solution.
        ii) The number of hydrogen ions is almost unchanged.

2. a) i)   **A**
        ii) The pH of solution **A** is lower, therefore the concentration of
             hydrogen ions is greater. The solution therefore has a greater
             degree of ionisation and is stronger.
    b) **A**
    c) **A**

d) i) 25 cm^3 of the same alkali

ii) As alkali is added, more acid molecules ionise until all the acid has been neutralised.

3. $$NH_4OH(aq) \rightleftharpoons NH_4^+(aq) + OH^-(aq)$$
When ammonium chloride is added to the ammonia solution, the equilibrium moves to the left. The concentration of OH$^-$(aq) falls and the pH of the solution is reduced.

4. Carbon dioxide dissolves in water to form carbonic acid, H_2CO_3. This is a weak acid which ionises to release hydrogen ions. The concentration of hydrogen ions increases and the pH of the solution decreases.

5. a) $$NH_3(g) + H_2O(l) \rightleftharpoons NH_4^+(aq) + OH^-(aq)$$

b) Unless the solutions are at the same concentration it is not possible to make fair comparisons of the relative concentrations of OH$^-$(aq) ions in solution since the potential number of ions which could form should be the same.

c) Sodium hydroxide is a strong base and is fully ionised in solution. The concentration of OH$^-$(aq) is high and the pH of the solution is also high. Since ammonia is a weak base, the concentration of OH$^-$(aq) in solution is much lower and the pH is lower.
Since sodium hydroxide is fully ionised. the overall number of ions in solution is high and therefore the conductivity is high, whereas ammonia solution contains relatively few ions and has much lower conductivity.
Both solutions will be neutralised by the same volume of acid, because the addition of acid causes the equilibrium in ammonia solution to move producing more OH$^-$(aq) ions in the solution until all the ammonia molecules have dissociated.

6. As sodium benzoate is added, the increase in concentration of benzoate ions is increased and the equilibrium moves to form undissociated benzoic acid. The concentration of H$^+$(aq) ions decreases and the pH of the solution increases.

Exercise 3.6 The pH of salt solutions

1. Sodium carbonate is the salt of a strong alkali and a weak acid, carbonic acid. When dissolved in water, H^+(aq) from water combine with CO_3^{2-}(aq) to form molecules of carbonic acid, H_2CO_3(aq). Since the concentration of hydrogen ions decreases, the pH increases to a value greater than 7.

2. a) The sulphonic acid is a weak acid.
   b) When sodium sulphonate dissolves, H^+(aq) from the water combine with sulphonate ions to form molecules of the sulphonic acid. Since the concentration of hydrogen ions decreases, the pH increases to a value greater than 7.

3.

pH less than 7	pH equal to 7	pH more than 7
ammonium sulphate	potassium chloride	sodium sulphite
ammonium nitrate	potassium nitrate	lithium carbonate
ammonium chloride	lithium sulphate	sodium ethanoate

4. a) HCN
   b) weak
   c) Potassium cyanide solution is aklaline. H^+(aq) from water combine with CN^-(aq) from the salt to form molecules of HCN. The concentration of hydrogen ions decreases and the pH increases to a value greater than 7.

Exercise 3.7 Oxidising and reducing agents

1. a) $2Al(s) + 6H^+(aq) \rightarrow 2Al^{3+}(aq) + 3H_2(g)$

   b) $2Ce^{4+}(aq) + 2Br^-(aq) \rightarrow Br_2(aq) + 2Ce^{3+}(aq)$

   c) $Cu(s) + 2Ag^+(aq) \rightarrow 2Ag(s) + Cu^{2+}(aq)$

   d) $MnO_4^-(aq) + 8H^+(aq) + 5Fe^{2+}(aq) \rightarrow Mn^{2+}(aq) + 4H_2O(l) + 5Fe^{3+}(aq)$

   e) $Cr_2O_7^{2-}(aq) + 14H^+(aq) + 3Sn^{2+}(aq) \rightarrow 2Cr^{3+}(aq) + 7H_2O(l) + 3Sn^{4+}(aq)$

2. a) $Cl_2(aq) + 2e^- \rightarrow 2Cl^-(aq)$
   $Fe^{2+}(aq) \rightarrow Fe^{3+}(aq) + e^-$

   b) $Zn(s) \rightarrow Zn^{2+}(aq) + 2e^-$
   $Cu^{2+}(aq) + 2e^- \rightarrow Cu(s)$

   c) $Mg(s) \rightarrow Mg^{2+}(aq) + 2e^-$
   $2H^+(aq) + 2e^- \rightarrow H_2(g)$

   d) $Cl_2(aq) + 2e^- \rightarrow 2Cl^-(aq)$
   $2Br^-(aq) \rightarrow Br_2(aq) + 2e^-$

   e) $Na(s) \rightarrow Na^+(aq) + e^-$
   $H_2(g) + 2e^- \rightarrow 2H^-(s)$

   f) $2S_2O_3^{2-}(aq) \rightarrow S_4O_6^{2-}(aq) + 2e^-$
   $I_2(aq) + 2e^- \rightarrow 2I^-(aq)$

   g) $MnO_4^-(aq) + 8H^+(aq) + 5e^- \rightarrow Mn^{2+}(aq) + 4H_2O(l)$
   $Cr^{2+}(aq) \rightarrow Cr^{3+}(aq) + e^-$

3. a) $SO_3^{2-}(aq) + H_2O(l) \rightarrow SO_4^{2-}(aq) + 2H^+(aq) + 2e^-$
   $I_2(aq) + 2e^- \rightarrow 2I^-(aq)$
   _____
   $SO_3^{2-}(aq) + H_2O(l) + I_2(aq) \rightarrow 2I^-(aq) + SO_4^{2-}(aq) + 2H^+(aq)$

   b) $2I^-(aq) \rightarrow I_2(aq) + 2e^-$
   $Cl_2(aq) + 2e^- \rightarrow 2Cl^-(aq)$
   _____
   $2I^-(aq) + Cl_2(aq) \rightarrow 2Cl^-(aq) + I_2(aq)$

   c) $MnO_4^-(aq) + 8H^+(aq) + 5e^- \rightarrow Mn^{2+}(aq) + 4H_2O(l)$
   $2Cl^-(aq) \rightarrow Cl_2(g) + 2e^-$
   _____
   $2MnO_4^-(aq) + 16H^+(aq) + 10Cl^-(aq) \rightarrow$
   $\qquad\qquad 2Mn^{2+}(aq) + 8H_2O(l) + 5Cl_2(g)$

   d) $Cr_2O_7^{2-}(aq) + 14H^+(aq) + 6e^- \rightarrow 2Cr^{3+}(aq) + 7H_2O(l)$
   $Fe^{2+}(aq) \rightarrow Fe^{3+}(aq) + e^-$
   _____
   $Cr_2O_7^{2-}(aq) + 14H^+(aq) + 6Fe^{2+}(aq) \rightarrow$
   $\qquad\qquad 2Cr^{3+}(aq) + 7H_2O(l) + 6Fe^{3+}(aq)$

   e) $MnO_4^-(aq) + 8H^+(aq) + 5e^- \rightarrow Mn^{2+}(aq) + 4H_2O(l)$
   $2Br^-(aq) \rightarrow Br_2(aq) + 2e^-$
   _____
   $2MnO_4^-(aq) + 16H^+(aq) + 10Br^-(aq) \rightarrow$
   $\qquad\qquad 2Mn^{2+}(aq) + 8H_2O(l) + 5Br_2(aq)$

4. a) $SO_3^{2-}(aq) + H_2O(l) \rightarrow SO_4^{2-}(aq) + 2H^+(aq) + 2e^-$
   b) $MnO_4^-(aq) + 8H^+(aq) + 5e^- \rightarrow Mn^{2+}(aq) + 4H_2O(l)$
   c) $2IO_3^-(aq) + 12H^+(aq) + 10e^- \rightarrow I_2(aq) + 6H_2O(l)$
   d) $2ClO_3^-(aq) + 12H^+(aq) + 10e^- \rightarrow Cl_2(aq) + 6H_2O(l)$
   e) $PbO_2(s) + 4H^+(aq) + 2e^- \rightarrow Pb^{2+}(aq) + 2H_2O(l)$
   f) $XeO_3(s) + 6H^+(aq) + 6e^- \rightarrow Xe(g) + 3H_2O(l)$
   g) $ClO^-(aq) + 2H^+(aq) + 2e^- \rightarrow Cl^-(aq) + H_2O(l)$

Exercise 3.8   Redox titrations

1. 0.150 mol   2. 0.16 mol l^{-1} 3. 0.086 g

4. 0.120 g   5. 24.9 g l^{-1} 6. 2.7×10^{-8} litre O_3 / litre air

7. 85.2%

Exercise 3.9   Electrolysis

1. 0.118 g   2. 8 g   3. 4.29 kg

4. 0.839 kg / min   5. 1206 s   6. 3+

7. 215 litres   8. 411 cm^3 9. 57.5 cm^3

10. 3.2 g   11. 24.1   12. 3.01×10^{23} electrons

13. 0.302 g

Exercise 3.10   Radioactivity

1. a) gamma
   b) alpha
   c) beta

2. a) i) So that radiation can escape in one direction only.

   ii) Beta particles are fast moving electrons and are strongly attracted towards the positive plate of the electric field.
   Alpha particles are helium nuclei and are attracted towards the negative plate of the electric field. since they are approximately 8000 times heavier than beta particles, they are deflected less by the same strength of electric field.
   Gamma rays are high energy electromagnetic radiation and are unaffected by electric fields.

   b) Because the ratio of protons to neutrons falls outside the band of stability.

3. Since alpha radiation is only weakly penetrating, the americium can be contained within a thin metal container which will prevent alpha rays from escaping into the living space of the occupants of the house. The half-life is relatively long, hence the level of radiation will effectively remain constant during the operational lifetime of the smoke detector.

4. Gamma radiation is extremely penetrating and would cause damage to cells in the patient's body.
   The half-life of the isotope is long, and if taken internally would expose the patient to radiation for a long time.

5. a) Organic material used to make artefacts such as clothing, tool handles, etc. contains a mixture of isotopes of carbon in the same proportion as they occur in the carbon dioxide in air. When the material is used, the ^{14}C isotope decays and the proportion of ^{14}C to ^{12}C falls at a rate characteristic of the ^{14}C isotope. By measuring the ^{14}C to ^{12}C ratio, the duration of the decay process can be estimated.

   b) Diamonds were formed in the Earth's crust from non-organic sources many millions of years ago. The original proportion of ^{14}C to ^{12}C is unknown and the period of decay is too great to estimate the number of half-lives which have elapsed, since the quantity of ^{14}C present will be negligible.

   c) The proportion of ^{14}C is so small after approximately 10 half-lives that estimates of age are very unreliable.

6. a) nuclear fission

   b) A tiny quantity of mass is converted into energy (e =mc^2) by the fission of each nucleus. The reaction accelerates rapidly since 2 neutrons are released by every fission. Enormous numbers of atoms break down releasing huge quantities of energy.

   c) For example, for thermonuclear bombs, for atomic power stations.

7. a) Uranium-238 has a very long half-life, close to the age of the Earth. The protactinium into which it decays has a very short half life of 6.75 hours and will decay rapidly after it has formed.

   b) Lead-206 is the final decay product of the decay of uranium-238.

8. a) nuclear fusion

   b) Nuclear reactions in the sun (and also hydrogen bombs).

9. a) A radioactive tracer is a radioisotope which can be used to follow a physical pathway or a chemical pathway by detection of the emitted radiation.

   b) For example, by putting a radioactive tracer into a stream which flows underground. The stream can be identified when it emerges above ground again.

10. a) For example, radioactive gold needles can be inserted into the thyroid gland to reduce the number of cells in the gland and reduce its activity.

    b) For example, cobalt-60 isotopes which emit gamma radiation can be used to detect flaws in the casting of metals to ensure that they will not fail in use.

Exercise 3.11   Nuclear equations

1. **y**   mass = 0   charge = -1   beta particle
   z   mass = 4   charge = +2   alpha particle

2. a) $^{24}_{12}Mg$ b) $^{238}_{92}U$

3. a) $^{210}_{84}Po \rightarrow {}^{206}_{82}Pb + {}^{4}_{2}He$

   b) $^{3}_{1}H \rightarrow {}^{3}_{2}He + {}^{0}_{-1}e$

   c) $^{226}_{88}Ra \rightarrow {}^{222}_{86}Rn + {}^{4}_{2}He$

   d) $^{90}_{38}Sr \rightarrow {}^{90}_{39}Y + {}^{0}_{-1}e$

4. a) $^{232}_{90}Th \rightarrow {}^{228}_{88}Ra + {}^{4}_{2}He$
   b) Th n/p ratio (1.578) is less than the Ra n/p ratio (1.591)

5. a) $\mathbf{X} = {}^{231}_{91}Pa$ $\qquad$ $\mathbf{Y} = {}^{227}_{89}Ac$
   b) $^{231}_{91}Pa \rightarrow {}^{227}_{89}Ac + {}^{4}_{2}He$ $\qquad$ α decay

6. The parent nucleus would suffer a net loss of 1 proton and 3 neutrons.

7. a) $^{238}_{92}U + {}^{1}_{0}n \rightarrow {}^{239}_{92}U$
   b) i) 8 $\qquad\qquad$ ii) 6

8. mass number 224, atomic number 88

9. $\mathbf{a} = 83$ $\qquad$ $\mathbf{b} = 215$ $\qquad$ $\mathbf{X} = Bi$

10. $^{210}_{83}Bi$

Exercise 3.12 $\qquad$ Artificial radioisotopes

1. a) Neutrons are readily available in nuclear reactors and, since they are neutral, are not repelled by the positive charges of nuclei.
   b) A beta particle would not produce a nuclear transformation without the absorption of huge quantities of energy.

2. a) $^{6}_{3}Li + {}^{1}_{0}n \rightarrow {}^{3}_{1}H + {}^{4}_{2}He$ $\qquad$ $\mathbf{R}$ is an α particle

   b) $^{238}_{92}U + {}^{4}_{2}He \rightarrow {}^{239}_{94}Pu + 3{}^{1}_{0}n$ $\qquad$ $\mathbf{S}$ is a neutron

3. a) **x** has mass 1 amu and charge +1   proton
   b) **y** has mass 1 amu and charge 0   neutron

4. a) **X** is lithium $p = 7$ $q = 3$
   b) **Y** is sodium $a = 23$ $b = 11$

5. $^{27}_{13}Al + ^{1}_{0}n \rightarrow ^{24}_{11}Na + ^{4}_{2}He$

   X is $^{24}_{11}Na$

   $^{24}_{11}Na \rightarrow ^{24}_{12}Mg + ^{0}_{-1}e$

   Y is $^{24}_{12}Mg$

6. $^{27}_{13}Al + ^{4}_{2}He \rightarrow ^{30}_{15}P + ^{1}_{0}n$

   Y is $^{30}_{15}P$

Exercise 3.13   Half-life

1. a) same   b) same   c) different   d) same

2. a) The time taken for half the number of atoms of a radioisotope to disintegrate.
   b) 0.781 g

3. 18 hr

4. 24 days

5. 6×10^{22} atoms

6. 12 days

7. 154.5 g

8.

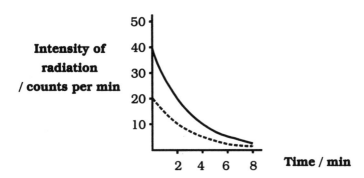

9. a) 3 min
    b) 1.3 min
    c)

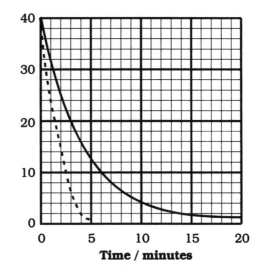

10. a) 1000 counts / min
    b) no change

11. 1 g samples of radium oxide and radium sulphate contain a different
    mass of radium and hence different numbers of radium atoms, therefore
    the number of disintegrations per second will be different.

12. 2 min

13. 3×10^{21} atoms

14. a) 15 hr
    b) 7 g

15. a) i) 12.5 years
        ii) 37.5 years
    b) no effect

16.*   a)

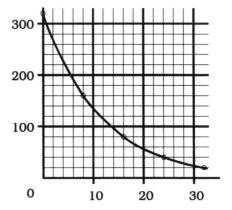

    b) 27 days

Prescribed Practical Activities

1. a)

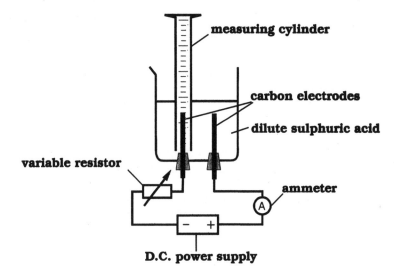

   b) volume of hydrogen produced at the negative electrode
       time of electrolysis experiment
       average current flowing through apparatus

2. a) To neutralise the sulphuric acid used to catalyse the reaction and any
       unreacted organic acid so that the hydrolysis of the ester formed
       cannot occur.
   b) The ester forms as an insoluble layer on top of the aqueous layer
       formed after the addition of sodium hydrogen carbonate solution.

3. a) initial and final masses of burner
       initial and final temperatures of water
       mass of water in beaker
   b) The apparatus was shielded to avoid draughts which would reduce
       the transfer of heat from the flame to the beaker.

4. a) 25.25 cm^3
   b) The starch indicator turns blue when no more iodine can be oxidised.

5. a) 6.7 °C (Assuming that equal volumes of sodium hydroxide solution and hydrochloric acid were used.)

    b) Solid sodium hydroxide would be added to water. The initial temperature of the water, and the maximum temperature of the solution after the addition of sodium hydroxide would be measured.

6. Step 3. Add a few drops of concentrated sulphuric acid.
    Step 4. Place in a bath of cold water and heat until the mixture reaches its boiling point. Turn off the source of heat.

7. a) catalase

    b) By measurement of the volume of oxygen liberated by the decomposition of hydrogen peroxide in a fixed time.

8. a) The discrepancy between result 1, and results 2 and 3, is greater than the acceptable limit of accuracy of the titration.

    b) For example:
    failure to wear eye protection
    failure to remove the funnel from the burette
    failure to use a pipette filler
    burette stand unsuitable (unstable)
    reading being taken from a burette from the wrong angle
    protective clothing is not giving protection
    pipette placed where it could roll off the bench

9. a) The volume of hydrochloric acid solution used in the experiment.

    b) Carry out the reactions in an expanded polystyrene beaker to avoid heat loss by conduction.

10. a) The starch indicator would turn blue-black.

    b) The first titre is outside the limit of acceptable experimental error.

11. a) To reduce the iodine liberated back to iodide ions so that the solution turns blue-black when equal numbers of moles of iodine have been liberated in a series of experiments using different concentrations of hydrogen peroxide.

    b) To show when free iodine is present in the solution.

12. a)

Mixture	1	2	3	4	5
Volume of sulphuric acid / cm³	10	10	10	10	10
Volume of sodium thiosulphate / cm³	10	10	10	10	10
Volume of starch / cm³	1	1	1	1	1
Volume of potassium iodide / cm³	25	20	15	10	5
Volume of water / cm³	0	5	10	15	20

b)   The starch turns blue-black.

13. For example:
Measure the temperature of the mixture at the start and finish of the experiment to find the average temperature at which the experiment takes place.
Add oxalic acid to the mixture and simultaneously start the timer.
Repeat the experiment at 40 °C for 3 readings and calculate the average reaction time.
Repeat the experiment over a wider temperature range, e.g. from 30 °C to 60 °C at 10 °C intervals.
Use pipettes to measure the volumes with greater accuracy.

14. a)

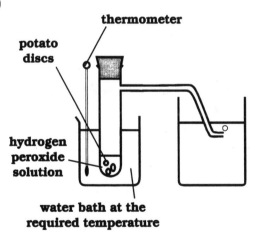

b)   "Approximate temperature" implies that the temperature of the experiment should be close to the required temperature but that it is not necessary to make measurements at precisely that temperature.

"Accurately" means that the temperature used for the experiment should be measured with the greatest degree of precision available to the experimenter.

15. a) concentrated sulphuric acid

   b) The reaction mixture can be neutralised using sodium hydrogen carbonate solution and the ester, formed as a separate layer, can be removed using a separating funnel, dried and purified by distillation.

16. a) " Initially the reaction mixture is purple in colour due to the presence of **permanganate** ions, but it will turn **colourless** as soon as they are used up."

   b) $1cm^3$ of oxalic acid, concentration 0.2 mol l^{-1}

   c) The temperature of the reaction mixture.
      The time taken for the mixture to become colourless.

17. a) for example, acidified potassium dichromate solution, Benedict's solution, Tollen's reagent

   b) The observations in the same order would be:
      turns from orange to green
      turns from a blue solution to a brick-red precipitate
      turns from colourless to deposit a silver mirror on the container

   c) They are volatile and flammable.

   d) For example, avoid naked flames, carry out the experiment in a fume cupboard.

18. a) Place the measuring cylinder above the negative electrode.

   b) the volume of hydrogen produced,
      the time taken to produce the hydrogen gas

Problem Solving

1. a) **A**   sodium hydroxide solution
       B   sodium hydroxide solution
       C   aluminium oxide
   b) **X**   digestion   **Y**   filtration   **Z**   roasting

2. **A**   ammonia (oxygen)   **B**   oxygen (ammonia)
     C   nitric oxide   **D**   water
     E   nitrogen dioxide   **F**   oxygen
     G   sulphurous acid   **H**   sulphur (air)
     I   sulphur dioxide   **J**   air (sulphur)
     K   water

3.

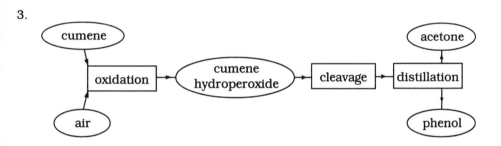

4. a)   tetra-atomic   b)   ethene   c) CH_2Cl_2

5. a)   the number of double bonds formed to oxygen
   b)

$$H-O-Cl{\nwarrow}^{O}_{O}$$

6.

     H H H   H H H   H H   H
     | | | | | | | | |
H—C —C —C — OH   H—C —C —C —H   H—C —C —O —C—H
     | | | | | | | | |
     H H H   H OH H   H H   H

7. **A** sodium sulphate(VI)   **B** KIO_3 **C** +5
    D sodium phosphate(V)   **E** −3

8. a)

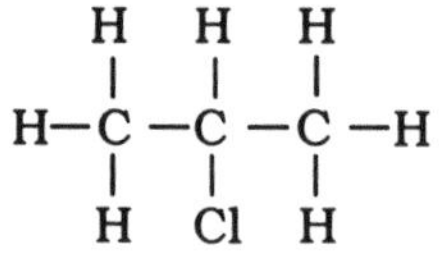

H H H
H−C−C−C−H
H Cl H

    b) Whichever way the hydrogen chloride adds across the double bond,
       the product formed will be the same, 2-chlorobutane.

9. a) **P** 6   **Q** Cu^{2+} **R** 4−   **S** $H_2N-CH_2-CH_2-NH_2$
    b) i) Make up solutions of nickel(II) sulphate and ammonia containing
            $9\ cm^3$ of nickel(II) sulphate and $1 cm^3$ of ammonia, $8\ cm^3$ of
            nickel sulphate and $2\ cm^3$ of ammonia, etc. and measure the
            intensity of the light transmitted through the solution.
        ii) 6.14

10. a)

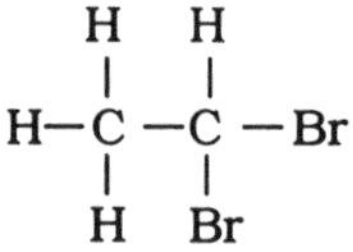

    b)

    c)

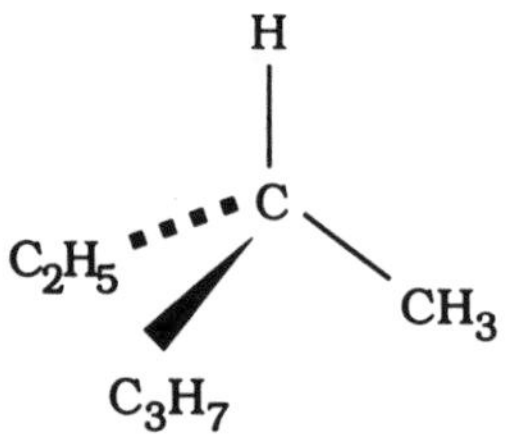

11. a) **F** $CH_3CH(OH)$ **G** $CH_3CH_2CH(OH)$

  b) The loss of hydrogen atoms from the carbon atoms of the $CH_3CH(OH)$ fragment.

12. a) The electron density round hydrogen nuclei is very low.

  b) 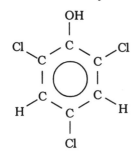   c)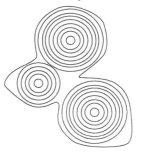

13. a) $-C=O$

  b) 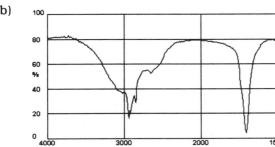 **wavenumber cm^{-1}**

14. a) The temperature of the test thermocouple is higher than the temperature of the reference thermocouple. Therefore the decomposition has released energy, and the reaction is exothermic.

  b) It must be stable to heat over a large temperature range.

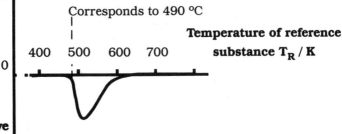